# Contents

# Acknowledgements

The following individuals and organisations have generously offered their time, expertise or permission to use already published materials so that they can benefit those working in the field of dementia:

All the Alzheimer's Society branches across the UK, which have generously shared their ideas and experiences and sent them in to the national office. We have not been able to use every idea contributed, but the large majority have been included in this book.

The Alzheimer's Association, USA, for permission to use material from their publication *Activity programming for persons with dementia: a sourcebook*

Madeline Andersen-Warren, dramatherapist, for many of the exercises used in the 'Movement and drama' chapter

Christine Bleathman and Murray House Mental Health Resource Unit, for the 'Your version of an old master' activity and their sunflowers picture

Martin Cobley, for the 'Gardening' chapter

Janice Emmott, massage therapist, for the 'Massage' chapter

Sylvia Gaspar, NAPA

Colin Harrison, volunteer co-ordinator, Newfield House, ExtraCare Charitable Trust

Sue Heiser, dementia development worker, Royal Borough of Kensington and Chelsea

Helen Malcolm, activity organiser, Barton House Nursing Home, Luton

Jacky Mortimer, freelance trainer

Marlene Rolfe, artist

Linda Rose, from Music for Life

Catherine Ross, musician and social worker

Pam Schweitzer, from Age Exchange

Speechmark Publishing

The residents, day centre members and staff of Thamesbrook Nursing and Residential Home and Edenham Day Centre, Royal Borough of Kensington and Chelsea

THRIVE

Th
bo

**Writ**

Sally
worl
spec
the I
Peop
in de



The Alzheimer's Society book of activities

ISBN 1 872874 72 X

Alzheimer's Society
Gordon House
10 Greencoat Place
London SW1P 1PH
Telephone 020 7306 0606
Fax 020 7306 0808
Email info@alzheimers.org.uk
Website www.alzheimers.org.uk
Registered charity no. 296645
A company limited by guarantee and
registered in England no. 2115499

Design and illustration

# Foreword

'Doing' is what life is all about for most people. Everyone, in their own way, makes things happen and leaves their mark. Most of us do this every hour of every day of our lives.

For people with dementia, the energy and the desire to continue doing things may be no different. It is their ability to organise, plan, initiate and successfully complete the tasks of daily life that changes.

The Alzheimer's Society believes that activity is an essential part of everyone's daily existence. Involvement in activity can help reduce the feelings of isolation often experienced by people with dementia, as well as increase people's confidence and provide opportunities for individual expression. Activities build upon people's strengths and abilities, and help to maintain a sense of identity and purpose.

This book has been written by professionals working in the field of activities, ranging from drama and movement to massage. It also includes contributions from Alzheimer's Society branches. It contains practical guidance, hints and suggestions for activities for people supporting those with dementia.

I hope that you will find this activity book informative, challenging, easy to use and, above all, fun!

Chief executive
Alzheimer's Society

Section 1

# Introduction

# Introduction

This book is mainly targeted at care workers in day care or residential settings. However, it includes many activities that relatives and friends or home/respite carers could try out with individuals. The chapters 'Everyday things to do at home' and 'Making the most of your local community' are particularly relevant for one-to-one work, but many of the activities in other chapters, such as 'Food, fun and parties' or 'Gardening', could be tried by a relative or care worker in a person's own home.

The chapter headings should help you to find activities of interest to specific individuals and groups. However, some of the topic areas overlap and might be of wider interest. For example, there are many ideas in the 'Everyday things to do at home' chapter that could also be used in care settings, and the 'Activities in the later stages of dementia' chapter might also be relevant to those working with people in the earlier stages of dementia. Whilst there is a specific 'Reminiscence and life history work' chapter, many of the activities in other chapters offer opportunities to reminisce.

**To get the most out of this book, you need a good understanding of dementia, sensitivity to and knowledge of the individuals in your care, and the enthusiasm and integrity to ensure that good ideas are translated into best practice.**

We recommend that you read the first section of this book, to remind yourself of the grounding principles for all activities work, before reading the chapters about specific activities.

This book contains only a relatively small selection of possibilities. We have not, for example, included ideas for holidays for people with dementia. The area of intergenerational and reminiscence work has been covered in detail in other publications, referred to in the 'Useful publications and resources' section.

The horizons for creative activity with people with dementia are ever expanding. We should focus our minds on the many and varied ways in which we can improve the lives of people who have dementia through involvement in activity.

Sally Knocker, 2002

# Thinking about activity

Below are some of the things to consider when planning an activity for people with dementia:

## What do we mean by activity?

Too often, activities are seen only as recreational events such as outings, concerts or carpet bowls, which are separated from the rest of daily life. This approach means that the potential for meaningful activity in everyday tasks such as cooking, cleaning, bathing and so on can be missed. For example, you can add a whole range of activities to mealtimes if you include people with dementia in the planning, the shopping, the preparation, the cooking and the clearing away, as well as the eating!

Formal activity programmes, such as those often provided by day centres, can be excellent, and many of the activities in this book can be used as part of such a programme. However, activity programmes must be supplemented by the use of age-appropriate activities *as part of everyday life*.

There are two important points to be made about the example below. The first is that people often don't realise quite how much they are doing – perhaps you are already doing more than you think! The second is that activities should not always consist of leisure or entertainment opportunities; the most effective activities often involve everyday tasks and involve a person's everyday occupations and feelings of self-worth.

EXAMPLE

## Creative activity work in practice

A day centre organiser was quite apologetic to visitors about the fact that the centre was not providing enough 'activities' for their members – they had very little in the way of a standardised programme. However, on closer inspection the day centre staff members were, in fact, being extremely creative about the way in which they involved people in the daily life of the centre.

Each morning, two of the people attending the centre went with a member of staff to the shops to buy a newspaper. They enjoyed the walk, the chat with the shopkeeper and the feeling of having done a useful job when they returned with the papers. Mr Bradbury enjoyed doing a simple daily crossword and a member of staff, who was also keen on crosswords, helped him to continue to do this. Phyllis, a woman who had limited verbal communication, loved watering and tending to the plants – she had owned a flower shop for many years and loved flowers. Margaret and Mrs Patel helped to prepare and serve morning teas and coffees. Albert, who had always been the 'drier up' at home, enjoyed drying the cups and saucers. Several members enjoyed betting on the horses and they often watched a race on the television in the afternoon. Mrs Rosari still played the piano beautifully if a member of staff gave her the first few lines of a song, and so she also was able to make a rich contribution to the atmosphere of the day centre.

The following are all important benefits of activity and occupation. Most people enjoy these benefits every day, simply through carrying out their usual routines and tasks. We must ensure that people with dementia have the same opportunities. This can be achieved through the provision of everyday activity.

## Benefits of activity

**Conversation and company** – an aspect of social life that gives us feelings of contact, companionship and belonging. People with dementia might need help with initiating a conversation or relaxing in a group of people.

**Variety and choice** – essential for keeping people's minds and bodies engaged in activities and for building feelings of self-esteem.

**Movement and physical exercise** – vital for the maintenance of good health and well-being. It is important to build exercise into the daily routine of people with dementia in as many ways as possible.

**Opportunities to feel busy or useful** – to counteract the feelings of incompetence or uselessness that many people experience as their dementia progresses.

**Engagement of the senses** – many older people have reduced hearing, sight or smell, and this should be taken into account when planning activities. A person's sight can be engaged through looking at photographs or pictures, and their hearing stimulated through listening to different kinds of music.

**Stimulation of the mind and memory** – long term memory is better preserved in people with dementia. Topic based discussions and quizzes can be enjoyable ways to engage people's intellect and stimulate their mind.

**Giving and receiving of affection** – often difficult for older people whose partners have died and who may also have lost close friends and relatives. The opportunity for intimacy and sexual expression is also an important need for some people with dementia.

**Connection with/interest in the outside world** – the world can feel smaller for a person who gets out and about less than they used to. People might need support from workers and family members to feel in touch with what is going on around them.

**Creativity and self-expression** – often expressed through long-standing hobbies or new interests such as painting, preparing food, gardening or knitting.

**Fun, laughter and play** – dementia can cause a lack of inhibition, which can 'free' a person's playful spirit and sense of humour. Moments of laughter and play can enhance a person's well-being.

**Religious faith and/or spiritual well-being** – often particularly important for a person who is experiencing losses and difficulties. A person's spiritual well-being can be sustained in many different ways – for example, by sitting quietly in a garden watching the sunset, or by listening to a beautiful piece of music.

# Assessing people's needs and abilities

To ensure that activities are appropriate for the people in your care, you should carry out detailed care assessments and draw up care plans for each person using your service. Assessments should include information about each person and their history, likes, dislikes, skills and abilities. Further information about how to carry out person-centred care assessments is available from the Alzheimer's Society.

Historically, most care plans have focused on problems and advised on how to meet health care needs. The social and activity-based needs of people with dementia have not been considered so thoroughly.

However, in order to get the most out of care plans, you should use them to detail people's strengths and interests in a specific and practical way. You can acknowledge any 'problems', but you should use the person's abilities and interests to plan their care, particularly in the area of activity.

By building on strengths, the picture of a person immediately becomes much more positive and optimistic, which in turn helps staff to start thinking about what is possible rather than what is difficult.

A strengths-based approach can also sometimes enable you to turn a 'problem' into a positive activity, as the example below demonstrates:

EXAMPLE

## Albert Potter

Albert started picking up objects from all over the day centre and hiding them where no one could find them. These objects included a television, a fire extinguisher and several other members' walking frames.

There were issues for concern here, particularly with the risks involved in losing the use of the fire extinguisher and other peoples' access to their walking aids.

However, this behaviour also highlighted clear strengths, involving Albert's abilities and independence:

'Albert retains a great deal of physical strength and has always been a man who prefers to keep physically active and busy. He was a joiner by profession and also liked gardening. He tends to move lots of objects around the centre. He always seems to be extremely content and absorbed in this activity.'

This version of the same events puts a much more positive light on the 'problem' presented.

The care workers decided to find other ways of using Albert's physical abilities, giving him work to do in the centre. They found objects that it was safe for Albert to move, and they enlisted his help – for example, with moving chairs in an empty meeting room. They also put piles of books or wood blocks on tables for Albert to pick up and move.

The care workers also investigated the possibility of Albert doing some digging in the garden, and they talked to the handyman about ways to involve him in some carpentry work.

Staff members realised that some of these ideas might not work, partly because Albert seemed to enjoy the independence and spontaneity of moving around the centre picking things up of his own accord. They understood that a care worker might have to walk closely but tactfully behind Albert and return items to their original places, once he had lost interest in them.

The staffing implications of this increased supervision had to be carefully considered.

## Monitoring and reviewing care plans

As dementia is a progressive condition, it is important to frequently re-evaluate the situation and the approaches that you are using. Check that the person's care plan is still appropriate at least once a month, or more frequently if their circumstances or needs change.

**There is a danger in assuming that a person still benefits from an activity just because it used to be closely linked to one of their interests.**

**For example:**

- **Arthur must like going to the local pub for a pint, because he did it for 40 years.**
- **Mrs Billow is likely to enjoy the art sessions because she was a professional artist.**

**People can become frustrated by continuing an activity that they used to do competently and independently. Involvement in art for Mrs Billow could be a painful reminder of her reduced skill and confidence.**

**A formal review should take place at least every six months and also whenever there is a significant change in the person's circumstances.**

# Using activity to meet psychological needs

Activities help to meet a person's deeper psychological needs. The psychologist Tom Kitwood described a cluster of needs, which overlap and come together in the central need for love. The fulfilment of one of these needs will contribute towards the fulfilment of the others, as they are closely linked.

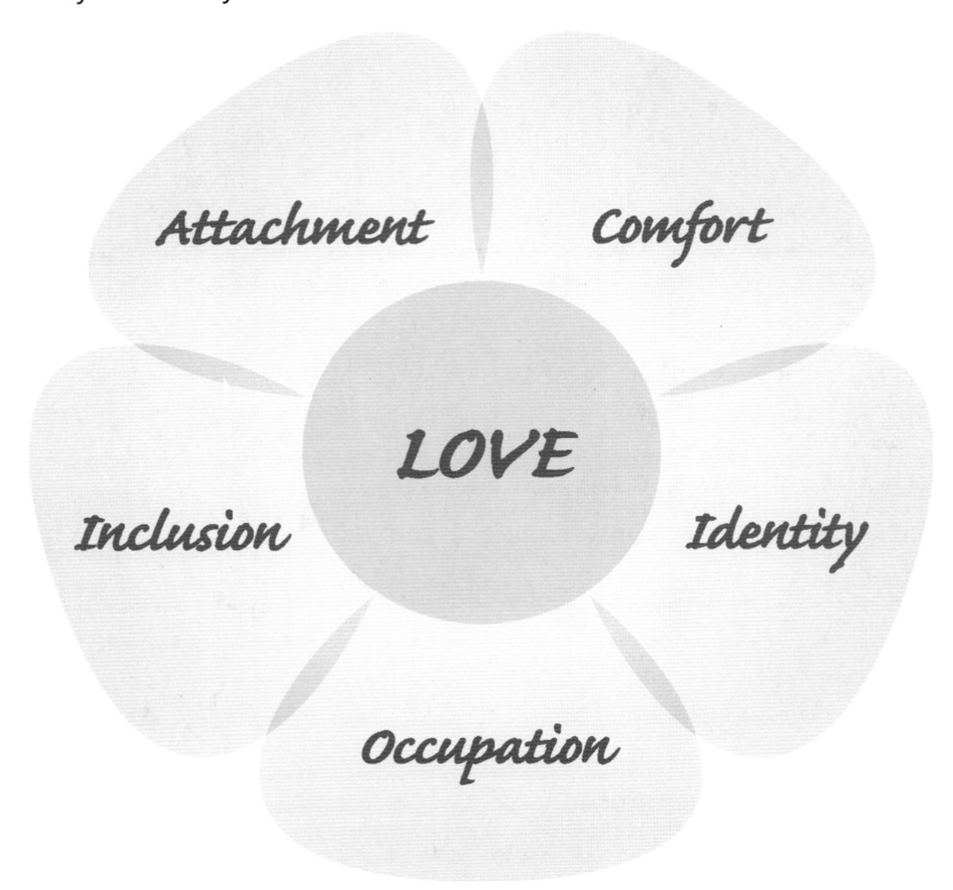


Adapted with permission from *Dementia reconsidered – the person comes first* by Kitwood, T, 1997, Open University Press, pp81-84

## The need for *comfort*

To provide comfort for a person is to provide warmth and strength to support them in a time of need. A person who has dementia is likely to experience loss and change, and will need comfort.

Many activities can comfort a person, particularly those that involve contact with others – for example, hugging a child, holding someone's hand or stroking a dog. Soaking in a warm bubble bath or having a gentle hand massage may also be comforting. Some people might get comfort from religious activity or from looking at a photograph of a loved one.

## The need for *attachment*

People with dementia can experience considerable uncertainty and often have to cope in 'strange' new situations. Their need for safety and security can be heightened.

A sense of safety and security is often found through attachments to people or objects, and can be expressed through intense preoccupations with items like handbags, keys or pieces of clothing. People may sort through their handbag regularly, to reinforce a sense of security and control over their life.

## The need for *identity*

We all have different ways of describing our identity. Some people define themselves by their relationships with others – for example, 'I am a mother' or, 'I am a wife'. Other people place greater emphasis on their race, nationality, religion or sexuality: 'I am Jewish', 'I am gay'. Our identity gives us a feeling of continuity between the past and the present and tells a 'story' about our life and the things that matter to us.

It is especially important to respect a person's identity when they are facing cognitive impairment. We need to know enough about their life history to be able to hold their sense of identity if and/or when their memory starts to fail.

It is essential to consider a person's sense of identity when choosing activities for them. A person's religious identity, for example, might be upheld by supporting them in observing that religion's rituals or traditions. If a woman's sense of identity centres on her role as mother of six children, reminiscence and life history work affirming the achievements and joys of this might support her well-being.

## The need for *inclusion*

People with dementia often find themselves feeling isolated, even in a crowd. Good care practice involves making a person feel included. When running an activity group in a large room, for example, be aware of people sitting on the fringes of the group or in the corner of the room. Even if they choose not to participate actively, make sure they are able just to watch and feel that they are part of the group.

## The need for *occupation*

Many of the occupations of daily life, such as tidying up, shopping or reading the paper, become more difficult for older people in care settings. Some people try to occupy themselves by walking around, picking objects up or playing with an item of clothing. Try to recognise when this kind of occupation is an expression of boredom or frustration and when the person is happily absorbed and content.

If the person seems to be bored or frustrated, help them find some purpose in an activity. For example, go for a walk in the garden with them or help them to collect the plates and put them back in the cupboard.

However, if they seem to be positively occupied, don't disrupt them and try not to label their behaviour as problematic or meaningless.

# Preparing for activity

## Organising a group

When getting people together in a group, consider any factors that might affect how they will get on. It is easy to assume that people from similar cultural or social backgrounds will have more in common. Although this is not always the case, many of us like to spend time with people who are 'like us'.

For British people in particular, an understanding of someone's cultural identity is also likely to include reference to social class. In care settings, there can be a tendency to avoid explicitly acknowledging a person's class background although this can be relevant to an understanding of the person and their interests.

Some day centres and care homes particularly neglect the needs of very well-educated people, who miss conversations and activities relating to their education and life experience. Such people can be perceived as being disinterested in group activities, when the problem is that these activities are not relevant to their cultural or class background.

However, people in day centres or care homes often come from a wide variety of backgrounds. Whilst some people are drawn towards people from similar backgrounds, some unlikely friendships form, cutting across age, class and culture.

Try to ensure that people don't feel isolated. This can happen if people feel different from everybody else; for example, if they are the only man in a group of women, the only gay person, the only person who speaks Spanish as their first language or if they are younger than everyone else.

Some practitioners, particularly in nursing and occupational therapy, recommend grouping people according to the 'stage' of dementia they are in. These stages are defined in various textbooks. It is generally suggested that as a person's dementia progresses, activities become less reflective and cognitively demanding, and more sensory and physically close to the person's immediate vision and hearing. If people with a similar level of dementia are grouped together, it is suggested, those in the early stages of dementia will not become unsettled or distressed by people with more advanced dementia. Staff will also find it easier to focus activities at the right level, rather than trying to respond to a wide variety of needs and abilities.

The danger of this kind of 'stage' approach is that it can categorise people too rigidly. It is very difficult to assess what 'stage' a person is in. They may appear to be in the advanced stages of their illness because they are very physically impaired when their mental abilities, however, are still relatively strong. There is also a danger in equating, for example, verbal ability with overall cognitive functioning; the ability to process speech does not necessarily reflect general cognitive abilities. Dementia affects people in very different ways and it is difficult to fit people into neat stages. However, for those who are interested in a more developmental approach to activity, the occupational therapist Jackie Pool has devised an assessment tool to help people ascertain what stage a person with dementia is in and to choose activities accordingly (see 'Useful publications and resources' on page 157).

Whilst there is a general movement towards dementia specialist services, these are not necessarily best for everyone.

EXAMPLE

Mrs Polari has vascular dementia. She has some insight into her increasing memory loss, which is causing her much anxiety. She became extremely distressed when she was with other people with dementia, especially when one man kept wandering over to her table and picking up food from her plate. When she moved from the dementia specialist unit to the general residential care unit, she became much happier. Because she is physically relatively fit, she helps some of the other residents who use wheelchairs and she helps to serve meals. She now rarely refers to her memory problems.

## Size of group and staffing ratios

The number of people taking part in a group activity will vary depending on the levels of need in the group, the type of activity and the experience and skill of the group leader and supporting staff.

If an activity requires some individual focus – for example, an art or gardening activity, a smaller number of people (between three and six) is appropriate. A music or drama group could benefit from having more people in it (perhaps eight to ten).

It is difficult to make an activity involving over 12 people work, unless the group is broken down into smaller groups. For example, groups of participants can sit around small tables, with individual workers, to play a game of bingo.

Sometimes the best activities do not take place in groups, but in pairs. Dividing a two-hour activities period into 10- to 15-minute slots of one-to-one time can work well. While one member of staff runs the one-to-one sessions, another member of staff can informally support the rest of the group.

# Structuring an activity session

People often plan 'games groups' or 'reminiscence groups' and so on as activity sessions for people with dementia. Sometimes, however, it is better to include different types of activity in one session. This can help to hold people's interest. The format offered below illustrates this kind of structure, and emphasises the need for a proper beginning and end to the session.

## Things to consider beforehand

- Where will the group be held – for example, would the main sitting area, a smaller quieter room, or the garden be best?
- Who might want to be involved?
- How many staff members are needed to run the group? Consider the special needs of people with hearing or visual impairments – they might need one-to-one support. Who will be the group leader?
- How will you present the session to participants? What will you do if they say 'no' initially? How can you get them interested?

## Sample structure of a group

### The beginning

- Play music as people arrive.
- Create a warm beginning – welcome and include everyone.
- Do introductions – this is worth it even if people know each other. Most people with dementia find it comforting and familiar to say their own name. If someone isn't able to say their name, welcome them personally by name.
- Have a chat about the day – this can include the weather, general news and what's happening.

### The core activity of the group

Try to include a mix of physical and mental activities and spend no more than about 10 to 15 minutes on each. Here are some examples of things you could do. Go to the relevant chapters for more ideas.

| Stimulating the mind | Stimulating the body |
|---|---|
| Conversation topics, such as: 'If you had a million pounds, what would you spend it on?' or, 'Is it wrong to have sex before you are married?'<br><br>Quiz questions<br><br>Reminiscence on a specific topic or theme, with some objects or pictures to prompt discussion<br><br>Newspaper or poetry reading with discussion | Exercise to music or a dance or drama activity<br><br>A game or other physical activity<br><br>An art, cooking or gardening activity (these are likely to take longer)<br><br>A sensory activity – a massage, looking at and touching fabrics, or polishing |

### Closing circle

- Ask whether people have enjoyed themselves.
- Sing a few songs.
- Do a closing ritual, such as making a wish for the day, or linking hands to say goodbye and thank you to each other. This might sound sentimental, but many people with dementia appreciate opportunities to enjoy warm contact with other people.

### When the group has ended

- Check what mood people are in.
- If the atmosphere is still upbeat, put some music on and encourage a lively and sociable atmosphere.
- If the atmosphere is quieter, ask where people want to sit. They might want to stay with the rest of the group for a while, or sit on their own and relax.
- Talk to colleagues about how the session went – what went well, what was difficult, do they think anybody didn't enjoy it?
- Consider whether you should add anything to any care plans as a result of the session.

# Making the environment 'activity friendly'

Care homes can be rather tidy and sterile, lacking in things to look at or talk about. If you look at your own home you will notice items that are often missing in institutional settings, such as a television guide, newspapers, fresh flowers, photographs or ornaments, easily accessible snacks and so on.

The care home or day centre environment should engage people's interest and stimulate their senses. Below and opposite are some ideas for furnishing or decorating bedrooms, lounges, corridors or reception areas.

### Ideas for furnishings and decoration

- Small groups of chairs in a living room encourage more social interaction than a large circle of chairs against the wall.
- A couple of chairs near a window (without net curtains!) can encourage residents to look outside and discuss what they can see there.
- A few chairs near the entrance or reception area enable people to enjoy the comings and goings of the place and chat to visitors.
- Provide coffee tables with a selection of magazines, newspapers, a television guide, balls of wool and knitting needles, and fresh flowers.
- Bookshelves should contain a wide selection of books, including large print novels, poetry collections, and illustrated books on a range of topics.
- Make sure there is an accurate large-faced clock in the lounge.
- Hang pictures low enough and make sure they are large and clear enough for people to be able to see and enjoy them. The subjects of the pictures should relate to the interests of some of the clients – for example, local places, animals or flowers.
- Corridors could have tactile or visually interesting objects and attachments along the walls, such as different textured fabrics, wooden or metal knobs, buttons to press (without setting off alarms!) and murals.
- A map of the world and a map of the UK on the wall can be effective prompts for informal reminiscence and conversation.

- Put an old-fashioned dressing table with a mirror, a chair and a selection of perfumes, aftershaves, make-up, jewellery and hair brushes in a bedroom. This enables residents to enjoy 'getting ready' in the morning.
- Mirrors can provide stimulation for people with dementia, although occasionally they can also cause distress.
- Develop a really good selection of music, which is clearly labelled – for example, 'party/dance music', 'gentle mealtime music', 'classical music', or 'energising foot-tapping music'.
- Shelves could hold interesting objects to look at or feel – for example, a ship in a bottle, Russian dolls or an old-fashioned musical box.
- An easily accessible cupboard containing cleaning materials such as dusters, a lightweight carpet cleaner and a dustpan and brush can encourage those who want to be involved with daily housework.
- Make sure your games or activity chest is easy for members of staff to dip into so that items *do* get used regularly.
- Put the television in a designated room or in the corner of the lounge rather than allowing it to dominate the main room. People can then make a choice about whether they want to watch it.
- Dining room tables can be used for group activities outside mealtimes. Removing tablecloths or condiments and putting out newspapers, pictures, board games or objects of interest can encourage this.
- Consider having an accessible snacks cupboard or fridge containing fruit, chocolate, cold drinks, crisps or biscuits. You may need to restrict access to this cupboard – for example, if someone is overweight or diabetic – but this is no reason to not have it! You could create a simple 'shop', which is open at particular times of the day. Some clients may enjoy having a role in running this shop.

**If you are working with people from different cultures, you need to think particularly carefully about the physical environment. Some cultures place more emphasis on religious observation, which might be reflected in pictures or symbols in the room.**

**It might be appropriate to have an office area or a workshop, where younger residents can feel as if they are still involved in working. Many older people might also benefit from this creative way of using the environment.**

**Ensure that pictures and types of music do not cater only for clients who are British and over 80.**

# Working with people from different cultures



Consider the cultural backgrounds of people and their carers when planning activities. Your awareness of other cultures will sharpen your understanding of each individual you have contact with.

Below are some ideas for how to make activities as appropriate and enjoyable as possible for everyone.

**A person from a different culture may feel homesick. Many people who came to Britain to work probably planned to go home – if this is no longer possible, they will need comfort and support.**

**The person may have experienced racism or persecution – find out who they feel safe with.**

**The person's sense of identity may be particularly fragile. Find out how you can support it. What has the person done in their life that you can reinforce?**

## Cultural considerations

- Consider the person's attitude to gender. Is the person used to being in mixed gender situations or are they used to segregation of the sexes for most activities such as eating, cooking and religious occasions?
- Does the person expect others to dress in certain ways (for example, covering upper arms) and do they feel uncomfortable if this is not the case?
- If an activity relies on reminiscence, does the person know about the events you are discussing? Could props that relate to the person's culture be used? For example, if you are talking about weddings, include some pictures of weddings in other cultures. See ideas for memory boxes for people from different cultures on page 96.
- Run a themed day about a festival from a different culture, such as Chinese New Year, Eid or Diwali. This may be very enjoyable and could involve an isolated person in your service. Use your local history libraries to find out about any local history of immigration.
- Offering alcohol to a person from a Methodist or Muslim background could cause offence – make sure you check first.

- Think carefully about activities involving cooking or food. Baking sausage rolls may not be ideal for everyone! Someone who is confused may not understand what they are eating, but their wishes must still be followed.
- Research music that the person can relate to – most public libraries have excellent world music sections.
- People may revert to their 'mother tongue', but also slip in and out of several languages. Many immigrants have learnt several languages in their country of origin or through moving around the world. You may need to use an interpreter. Learn some key words for greetings and expressions of respect.
- Check whether the written word is useful to a person. Some people may be illiterate in English but not in their original language – other people may be illiterate in both languages. Some people may read English much better than they speak it.
- People from some cultures are louder and more expressive in their usual communication than those from other cultures – this may not mean that a person is upset.
- Use signs and gestures to aid communication but find out about any gestures that might be considered rude in particular cultures.
- A lot of eye contact with your elders, or any contradiction of them, is seen as very disrespectful in many African and South Asian cultures.
- Touch may be much more common and expected in other cultures – although often not between genders. Make sure you find out.
- Common body language in some cultures can be misinterpreted as a sign of dementia. For example, rocking and repetitive talk is common in many Muslim countries and may be part of normal habits.

# Carrying out activities

## Some good practice principles

Dementia can affect the way a person understands and carries out activities in many different ways, depending on the type of dementia the person has and the person's character. It is vital, therefore, that you do not make assumptions about a person with dementia's abilities. Some of the ways in which dementia can affect a person's abilities are listed below.

### 1 Dementia often affects the ability to initiate an action

People with dementia may seem to be less willing to start or to join in an activity, although once they get going, they often enjoy themselves. It is also common for someone with dementia to get 'stuck' doing one thing, such as repeating the same phrase or question.

- When asking a person if they would like to join in an activity, be aware that using words might not be sufficient. You may also need to use music or non-verbal encouragement such as eye contact and physical gestures to prompt the person into getting involved or moving onto something new.

### 2 Dementia can have a major impact on a person's confidence

A lack of confidence often makes a person withdraw from social contact and show reluctance to take part in activities. This is often due to fear of failure or humiliation.

- Build on a person's strengths and use activities that are 'failure free'.
- Choose activities that focus on things a person is still able to do.

### 3 People with dementia can have difficulty with sustained concentration and attention

An activity that lasts for too long will not hold people's attention. People may try to get up and leave or start talking over each other.

- Make sure that group activities contain lots of variety so that people's attention is constantly refocused onto something new. If you are running a group for 45 minutes, for example, think of three or four 10 to 15 minute long activities to run within the session.

## 4 Dementia affects logical thinking, intellect and memory

Many activities can over-challenge these abilities. A crafts or cooking activity, for example, can be demanding because there is usually a sequence of tasks that must be understood and remembered. Games often have rules to be followed; a quiz requires memory and intellectual thought.

- Keep things clear and simple.
- Don't be too task-centred.
- Tap into long term memories, which will probably be more intact.
- Think about how an activity might make demands on a person's intellect, logical reasoning and memory.
- Be prepared to adapt the rules if a person is unable to carry out a task in the usual way. Be flexible.

## 5 Dementia can cause decreased inhibition

A person with dementia is more likely to say or do things instinctively, because the controls that monitor social behaviour are not as firmly in place.

This can be challenging when doing activities with a group of people, as they are more likely to get up and move away when the mood takes them, or to react strongly if something unsettles them.

A lack of inhibition also has positive aspects, however. A person might be more likely to have a go at something new, and be spontaneous without feeling as self-conscious as they used to.

- Be alert to the needs of individuals in the group and ready to respond to unexpected behaviour.
- Don't over-react to unpredictable behaviour, or automatically interpret it as a problem. For example, don't tell a person to sit down every time they get up to walk around. Try taking a stroll with the person and then returning to the group later.
- Enjoy and cultivate the spontaneous energy and enthusiasm that a person might bring to an activity. Be ready and willing to go with the flow!

## 6 Dementia can affect a person's spatial awareness and perceptual skills

Some games demand the ability to judge distances, colours, and shapes; these games can be challenging and frustrating for a person whose abilities in these areas are impaired. A game of dominoes, for example, although familiar to many people, is complex in terms of recognising and understanding the configuration of the dots, and understanding the concept of joining up matching pieces.

- Watch out for verbal or non-verbal clues that a person is struggling with an activity. For example, they might be irritable or fidgety or avoid eye contact.
- If a person is having difficulty understanding and following a particular activity, do not push them to continue.
- Be prepared to adapt an activity or move onto something different.

## 7 Dementia can affect a person's ability to understand and process language and to express themselves verbally

If someone has difficulty understanding what other people say to them, they may find it hard to relate to others in a group activity such as a discussion or quiz.

If a person has problems speaking, time and support can help them make themselves understood. Activities that place less emphasis on words, perhaps using music or objects to stimulate interest and involvement, can sometimes help a person's verbal fluency.

- Make sure you explain activities clearly and always allow people lots of time to consider the tasks they are going to do.
- Use gestures and body language as well as words to explain yourself.

Section 2

# Activities

# Everyday things to do at home

If you are caring for a relative at home, you have the advantage of knowing what they like and dislike and what their hobbies and habits are. However, the progression of dementia often means that a person's ability to engage in former pastimes diminishes. If you are exhausted and stressed by the demands of caring for someone all day, it can be hard to find the time or the energy for 'quality time' and stimulating activity. However, most family members who do try different ways of involving the person with dementia in activities at home report that it brings more pleasure and satisfaction to the relationship.

If you are a worker or a volunteer visiting a person in his or her own home, be aware that you are a guest. Be diplomatic and respectful about the extent to which you take a lead in suggesting activities. You may also need to discuss your ideas with the person's relatives, as this will give you a better idea of the person's past interests. Looking at some of the things in the person's home, for example, photographs and ornaments, may also give you an insight into their hobbies.

Many of the ideas for activity in this chapter are also tasks carried out in normal, everyday life. Perhaps you already do these kinds of things with your relative or client, but have not considered them as 'activities' before.

Although these activities are particularly suited to working with a person in their own home, they can also be used in residential homes and day centres if care staff consider the activities and their requirements carefully.

## Household tasks

A person's background will affect whether or not they enjoy doing household tasks. Many household tasks use well-preserved skills and can be managed by people with even a moderate level of dementia.

Do not be rushed or rigid about how household tasks are carried out. Be prepared to think creatively and to adapt the task to fit the ability level of the person. For example, many people with dementia find it easy to use a lightweight carpet cleaner, but might struggle with a modern electric vacuum cleaner. Be prepared to stand back and let the job be done without too much supervision. If the cups need a more thorough wash later, do it out of sight and tactfully. Make the most of the social contact involved in some of these jobs – for example, one person can wash up while the other dries, or you can both do the polishing together.

Think about jobs that can be done sitting down for people who are less physically mobile, such as folding small items or polishing, You could bring a washing up bowl to the person at a table so that they can do the washing up even if they are unable to stand at the sink.

The following are ideas for activities in the home:

- handwashing small items of clothing
- hanging out the washing
- ironing – with appropriate support and attention to temperature
- folding sheets, with one person at either end of the sheet, coming together to fold in sections
- dusting
- mopping the floor
- vacuuming
- polishing furniture
- tidying out drawers and wardrobes
- cleaning brass or silver
- washing/drying the dishes
- laying and clearing the table
- preparing vegetables – for example, shelling peas or peeling potatoes
- discussing the day's meals, looking at recipes together and writing a shopping list
- watering plants
- arranging flowers.

## Sorting

Sorting involves sight, touch and memory. Be careful with small objects, such as buttons and beads, if the person might put them in their mouth. If a person's dementia has affected their perceptual, organisational and logical skills, sorting in a systematic way might be too challenging. However, it may still be possible for them to enjoy the visual and tactile experience of picking items up, exploring and rearranging them.

The following items can be sorted:

- greetings cards and postcards
- pictures from magazines
- coins
- cutlery
- flowers
- stamps
- screws and keys
- socks or gloves
- junk mail
- chessmen
- beads and buttons.

## Tidying

Tidying and sorting through personal objects like handbags and drawers can provide good opportunities for conversation and reminiscence. People often also feel a sense of achievement when they have completed the task.

Some examples of things that can be sorted through and tidied include:

- a handbag
- a wallet
- a small drawer from a desk
- a toolbox
- a needlework box
- a specially created box of items that are familiar to or treasured by the person.

## Sewing and knitting

A good knitting or haberdashery shop will have a selection of tapestry sets and knitting needles that are easier for older people with impaired sight and manual dexterity to use. Even if people are no longer able to knit, they might enjoy watching another person knit and they may be able to give advice about colours and styles.

## Television and video

Television is often considered to be too passive as an activity for people with dementia. However, if used selectively, it can provide a useful addition to a range of activities in the home. Some people with dementia lose interest altogether in the television. Others might need your help to 'tune in' to what is happening – for example, if you are watching a news item, it may help if you comment on it.

The right programmes to choose will depend on the person with dementia and their background. Some people will enjoy a game show or quiz show, or a programme about animal rescue or wildlife. Others will prefer a historical documentary or a ballet.

If the person particularly enjoys a certain type of programme, don't be afraid to cheat and videotape some of it to replay another time. You could tape the highlights of sports events so that they can be watched again and again, even out of season.

Films or programmes with particularly animated music or visual effects are often particularly successful. Examples of these include the classic musicals and Celtic dance shows like 'Riverdance'. There are many good old classics on at Christmas or during the afternoons at the weekend.

The use of children's programmes or videotapes in dementia care is controversial. However, because children's programmes are often designed to be colourful and stimulating for young people, they can sometimes also captivate a person with deteriorating cognitive abilities. John Bayley described how Iris Murdoch watched the 'Teletubbies' with rapt attention and evident pleasure during the later stages of her illness. It is, however, inappropriate to switch on children's television for a person who may be unable to turn it off or to leave the room. If television is used in care homes, it is important that individual assessments, involving relatives where possible, are made.

You can also use a soft headset, which can be plugged into the television. This can help the person to pay attention because the sound is focused into their ears. However, if you use headsets or earphones be careful about the volume and watch for signs that the person is becoming frustrated or uncomfortable.

# Making the most of your local community

Make the most of the range of resources available in the community that can provide stimulation, interest and enjoyment to people with dementia. This can be achieved in very simple ways

EXAMPLE

## Using the local community

One day centre was very close to a registry office, and people in the centre would sometimes go and watch the married couples and their wedding parties come down the steps. This prompted much lively discussion about the clothes people wore, how happy the couple looked and memories of people's own weddings.

### Visiting places

Use your knowledge of the person or people in your care to find places to visit. Find out which places have been important to them in the past – for example, where they used to live, work or go to school. Talk to them and their relative/carer, if you work in a care home. Visit the place or area; walk or drive around. Engage the person in reminiscing by showing an interest and asking them questions about the place.

Here are some ideas for places that you could visit. These will vary enormously depending on whether you are based in the centre of a city or a remote rural location.

- adult education classes
- airports
- animal/bird sanctuaries
- aquariums, aviaries, fisheries
- arts centres, art galleries, exhibitions
- beauty salons
- betting shops
- bingo clubs
- bowling centres, bowling greens
- car boot sales
- children's playgrounds
- churches, cathedrals, synagogues, mosques, temples, gurdwaras
- cinemas
- city farms
- clubs, societies (think about individual interests)
- concerts
- dance clubs or groups – for example, ballroom, salsa, circle dancing
- dog shows
- fairs, fetes, craft fairs, circuses, theme parks
- farms or stables
- flying schools, sailing schools
- forests or woodland
- garden/vegetable allotments
- garden centres
- gymkhanas, horse shows
- hairdressers
- libraries
- markets
- museums
- National Trust, English Heritage or other houses, castles, historical sites open to the public
- orchards, fruit farms
- parks
- political parties or trade union clubs/associations
- ports, harbours, marinas
- public gardens
- pubs
- railway stations
- restaurants

- rivers/ponds/reservoirs/lakes/ waterfalls
- seaside or beaches
- shops – think of individual preferences – for example, clothes shops, department stores, book shops, chemist, DIY stores, bakers
- sports events or venues – for example, golf course, football stadium, race course
- sports or leisure centres
- swimming pools
- theatre/amateur dramatics performances
- wildlife parks
- zoos

**Be prepared for some areas to have changed beyond recognition.**

**People might feel put on the spot if you ask them too many questions. Give them time to recall and explore memories.**

**Visiting places of personal interest can provoke strong emotions. This is not necessarily a bad thing but you must be understanding and supportive so that the person does not feel overwhelmed or alone with these feelings.**

**Not everyone will get on well together; different personalities may need to be taken into consideration and seating arrangements made accordingly.**

## Things to consider when planning trips

### Transport

Many care homes and day centres do not have access to their own bus. However, you may be able to join a community transport organisation, befriend a local taxi firm or find volunteers with cars. If you use volunteers, it is important to check the insurance cover and the volunteer's driving record, and to assess whether people also need individual escorts.

### Staffing ratios

You will need more staff if people are going out of the building, especially if they are not independently mobile. A person with dementia often gets the most enjoyment from an excursion if they have one-to-one support and companionship. However, not all care homes or day centres can release a member of staff to spend time with just one person. Managers need to think of creative ways to release members of staff to do some of this vital work. Perhaps each member of staff could have a half-day every week or fortnight when they can go out with one or two of the residents. The manager may need to provide cover for the member of staff whilst they are out.

EXAMPLE

## Good practice in action...

Three men with dementia and their relief carer went on an outing to a local motor museum. Tom had worked in the motor industry and had been involved in making some of the gearboxes of models on show. John had owned a Honda scooter and was always talking about the pleasure he had with it. The third member of the group enjoyed outings and the company of others generally, without having a particular interest in motors.

Ingredients for success

The place chosen stimulated happy memories and was of specific interest to two of the men. The relief carer had been involved with all three clients for some time, which gave her an extensive knowledge of the men's interests, likes and dislikes. The group already knew each other, which helped them feel relaxed and confident together.

### Health and safety considerations

A risk assessment will need to be done for each person, considering their needs regarding balance, mobility, orientation, diet and medication. You will also need to consider what a person's psychological and emotional needs will be in a different environment. These needs may not become apparent until a small outing is attempted. If the person's reactions and well-being are carefully monitored during the trip and for a period after their return, you should be able to evaluate its benefit.

### Choosing a place, which is 'dementia and older people friendly'

Prepare for outings thoroughly and get people 'on your side' before you go along with a group of people. Phone beforehand to explain who you are and when you will be coming. Ask whether there is a particular person you should contact when you arrive.

You might have a great idea that you think will be perfect for an outing but that doesn't work out as you planned. Don't be put off by this – on a different day or with another person or group of people, it could be a great success.

Try to keep a sense of humour and humility about outings that don't work, as in the following account:

EXAMPLE

I decided to take Mum to Tropical World – a wonderful complex of linked greenhouses in a nearby park.... I steered her through a turnstile and at once we were in the glass tunnel of the aquarium. Mum was stunned. She stopped dead and returned the unblinking gaze of the assorted fish. Turning slowly to see all around, she asked with some bafflement, 'Where's this?'

'It's an aquarium, Mum. These are all tropical fish', I tried to explain. Saying nothing further, she marched through the tunnel at full speed. The next section annoyed her even more. It had small mammals and reptiles in pens, which reproduced their natural habitat. Mum now wore a distinct frown and her pace did not slacken. 'Don't like things in boxes,' she muttered.

A sudden horrid thought occurred to me – was this her perception of her own environment? Cursing myself for being an insensitive idiot, I hurried her through to the beautiful butterfly garden... I had thought Mum would find this as enchanting as I did and pointed out a particularly spectacular butterfly. She narrowed her eyes. 'Moths!', she said disdainfully. I realised that, for Mum, this was not the treat I had intended. I had overestimated her ability to cope with so many new things. It was information overload rather than a stimulating sensory experience.

(Judith Scott, Alzheimer's Society Newsletter, September 2000)

## Bringing the outside in

You can invite individuals and organisations from the local community into your day centre or care home. This can provide stimulation and variety to the day's activities, but can again present some challenges!

Persevere in your search for suitable visitors. Doing an initial 'map' of your area is a good start, and sometimes looking in a local telephone directory will give you ideas and contacts you had never thought of before. Also check local newspapers, literature in health centres or doctors' surgeries, leisure centre programmes and other voluntary organisations.

You may need to pay for some people's visits. However, it may be possible to find sponsorship from a local business or grant-giving trust to support such initiatives. It can also be helpful to give volunteers or visitors feedback about how their contribution is making a difference. If people feel appreciated, they are more likely to help again.

Here are some ideas for people and organisations that might be willing to visit a care home or day centre:

- adult education tutors
- ambulance service
- aromatherapists/massage therapists
- art teachers and therapists
- artists
- beauticians
- charities relating to particular interest areas (for talks)
- clubs, societies
- cooks
- dancers, dance movement therapists
- drama teachers and dramatherapists
- entertainers
- environmental organisations
- fitness/exercise professionals
- florists/flower arrangers
- guide dogs and trainers
- hairdressers
- leisure centre professionals
- mobile library services
- mothers and toddlers
- musicians, orchestras, bands, school or adult choirs
- National Trust/English Heritage for talks/slide shows
- occupational therapists
- pets and their owners
- police/police dogs and trainers
- politicians – MPs or councillors
- potters/pottery – for exhibition or demonstration
- reflexologists
- religious leaders
- sales representatives – for example, for specialist clothing or cosmetics
- schools/nurseries
- yoga teachers

**If a volunteer visitor has no prior experience of relating to a person with dementia, they might find it daunting. They may not know how to respond to muddled communication, repetitive questioning or someone who is withdrawn and unresponsive. Without support, encouragement and possibly training, they might feel 'useless' or that their visit was not worthwhile.**

**You may worry that 'outsiders' coming in will break up your routine and change the way you do things. However, contact with a range of different people can make a huge difference to people's lives without causing you undue stress. Develop your welcoming skills and ensure that visitors are always greeted, offered a drink and introduced to the people with whom they will be spending time.**

EXAMPLE

## A successful visit

Shirley and Max, her golden retriever, spent 20 minutes with Mrs Appleton, who used to be a dog trainer and loves animals. Mrs Appleton is now unable to walk independently and only says the occasional word. However, she brushed Max's coat and talked to him quite clearly and expressively; 'Aren't you beautiful! There's a good dog!' As Shirley and Max were leaving, Rashid, the care worker, said: 'That was wonderful, seeing Mrs Appleton so happy. She hardly ever speaks as much as that these days. Thank you so much for visiting! We look forward to your next visit'.

# Fun and games

Games are part of the culture of some families, but not of others – they will have positive and familiar associations for some people, but not for everybody. It is important to carry out individual assessments, but be aware that if someone didn't play games much as a younger person, it doesn't necessarily mean they won't enjoy them in later life!

Games with rules and sequences of actions may be difficult for some people to follow. Be prepared to adjust the rules and accommodate different abilities by changing the requirements of the game. Try not to worry about how things 'should' be done – the aim of these activities is to have fun!

# Skittles

## What is needed

- Wooden or plastic skittles – avoid children's toy versions; good quality equipment should always be used where possible. Wooden skittles are often more familiar to older people.
- Balls or bowls set – consider getting a range of sizes and weights so that people with less strength can also play. Alternatively, you can use beanbags.
- A 'V'-shaped chute of stiff card or a section of plastic guttering, to enable people with limited arm movement to roll the ball from their lap to the floor.

## How it is done

- Set up the skittles – this can be done by anybody who is physically able and might enjoy doing this useful job. Seat everybody at an appropriate distance from the skittles.
- Each person has a turn at throwing the ball at the skittles. The aim of the game is to knock down as many of the skittles as possible. If people are timid or reluctant, let them watch others have a go first. Individuals can play standing up or from a sitting position, depending on ability. If they prefer, people can roll the ball down the chute or guttering and onto the floor. Move the skittles to a distance at which success is most likely for each person and give people a second go if they are frustrated by their first effort.
- You can divide people into teams and keep score; this puts less pressure on individuals to succeed. However, some people might feel that they are 'letting their side down'.
- Encourage group awareness with gentle competition between participants. If you keep scores, provide small prizes for winners.

**People can watch each other's turns if they sit in a well spaced out circle. However, some people might feel uncomfortable being watched by others and a more individual and 'low key' approach might suit them better.**

**Don't overdo the number of rounds. Sometimes, people enjoy having one or two turns and then get fed-up or tired. Others might enjoy playing for much longer!**

## Variations

Indoor bowling is very similar. The aim of the game is to get the large ball(s) as close to the smaller target ball (usually black or a distinctive colour) as possible.

# The word game

## What is needed

- A whiteboard or flip-chart and some pens

## How it is done

- Seat the people playing within easy sight of the whiteboard or flip-chart and make sure that everyone is comfortable.

- Suggest a category – for example, 'cities' or 'animals', and ask members of the group to call out examples of things in that category. Write the suggestions on the whiteboard or flip-chart.

- This game should be used as a prompt for conversation. Try saying things about the words that people call out, such as, 'I remember when I first went to London', or 'I have always loved cats'. Give people time to respond to these comments – and to come up with their own!

- You can make the game more sophisticated by asking someone in the group to choose a letter of the alphabet. Think of some more categories, and then make a list of examples that start with that letter.

- For example, if someone chooses the letter 'S', write it in large print on the board. The categories could be countries, animals/birds/insects and food. Here are some examples of words that people could call out.

| Countries | Animals/birds/insects | Food |
|---|---|---|
| Spain | snake | spinach |
| Serbia | slug | sausage |
| Sardinia | spider | stew |
| Sierra Leone | sparrow | steak |
| Switzerland | sheep | spaghetti |
| South Africa | | sushi |
| Singapore | | sugar |
| | | sauce |
| | | spice |

- Encourage healthy debate where possible – for example, is spice a food? Is Sardinia a country?

- Other categories that you could use include:
  - flowers or trees
  - songs (encourage singing as you remember them!)
  - famous people
  - towns
  - jobs and professions

- Watch out for the person who suggests the letter 'X' with a cheeky smile, knowing that everyone will struggle to think of anything! If this happens, make the most of the humour and think creatively.

**Some people might need one-to-one support if they are hard of hearing or cannot see the board easily. They may need a member of staff to sit beside them and repeat or write down the letter and the category for them.**

**Use props to help people – for example, you could show a large map of the world or pictures of animals.**

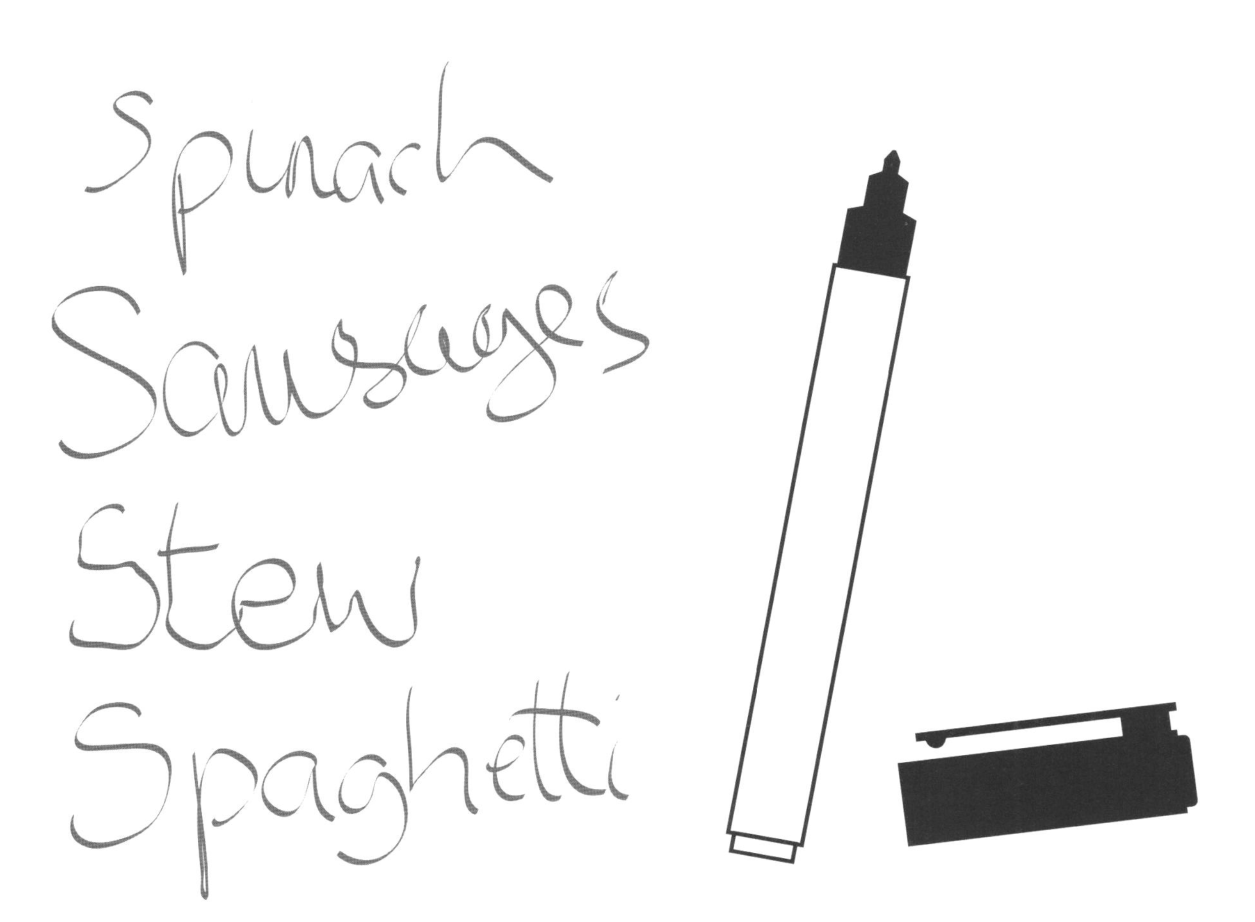

# Finish the proverb OR pair game

Sayings and proverbs are well learned and easily remembered by many people. They can be used in this 'failure free' type of quiz.

## What is needed

- A list of unfinished proverbs, sayings or pairs (see below).

## How it is done

- You say the first part of a saying or proverb from the list below, leaving out the part in brackets. The aim is for the other people playing the game to complete the missing part. Say the proverb clearly – you may need to repeat it a few times.

- You can ask each person in turn, or you can divide the group into small teams, to avoid putting pressure on individuals. However, this can mean that the quickest and most able person in each team responds every time.

**Dementia may affect a person's ability to explain the meaning of proverbs or sayings. Avoid asking anyone to explain the meaning of the sayings, unless you are sure that they know the answer.**

**Many of the sayings and word pairs listed below may not be familiar to someone who was not brought up in the UK. If you are working with people from other cultures, do some research into the sayings, proverbs or word pairs from their countries.**

**Some sayings have changed over the generations, so be flexible if you are given different answers to those offered here!**

**Consider the age of the people in the group. People born after the 1960s will have many different cultural associations than those of older people.**

**Choose proverbs or sayings according to the ability of individuals. Some are much better known than others.**

## Examples of sayings and pairs

**Easier and better known sayings**
Too many cooks (spoil the broth)
If you can't beat them (join them)
Birds of a feather (flock together)
Make hay (while the sun shines)
A stitch in time (saves nine)
Every cloud (has a silver lining)

All that glitters (is not gold)
Don't put all your eggs (in one basket)
A chip off the old (block)
Have a bee in your (bonnet)
There's no peace for the (wicked)
A bird in the hand is worth (two in the bush)
Sleep tight! Mind the bed bugs don't (bite)
There are plenty more fish (in the sea)
A watched pot (never boils)
The early bird (catches the worm)
The grass is always (greener on the other side)
Once bitten (twice shy)

**More difficult sayings**
All work and no play (makes Jack a dull boy)
People who live in glass houses (shouldn't throw stones)
Great oaks (from little acorns grow)
If you've made your bed (you must lie on it)
Horses sweat, men perspire, but ladies (glow)
The pen is mightier than the (sword)
Nothing ventured (nothing gained)
Time and tide wait for (no man)
All's ashore that's (going ashore)
A red letter (day)
Swing the (lead)
Haul over the (coals)
Rain, rain, (go away) – for a bonus point, finish the verse (come again another day)
That's for me to know and for you to (find out)

**Similes**

As thick as (two short planks)
As pleased as (punch)
As quick as (a flash)
As light as (a feather)
As quiet as (a mouse)
As mad as (a hatter)
As right as (rain)
As blind as (a bat)
As bright as (a button)
As deaf as (a post)
As long as (your arm)
As fresh as (a daisy)
As strong as (an ox)
As flat as (a pancake)
As cool as (a cucumber)

**Easier pairs**

Strawberries and (cream)
Bubble and (squeak)
Pie and (mash)
Bread and (butter)
Bacon and (eggs)
Fish and (chips)
Sugar and (spice)
Oranges and (lemons)
King and (Queen)
Birds and (bees)
Dustpan and (brush)
Cup and (saucer)
Salt and (pepper)
Bat and (ball)
Snakes and (ladders)

**People pairs**
Victoria and (Albert)
Romeo and (Juliet)
Darby and (Joan)
Rudolf Nureyev and (Margot Fontaine)
Gilbert and (Sullivan)
Tom and (Jerry)
Nelson Eddy and (Jeanette MacDonald)
Fred Astaire and (Ginger Rogers)
Robin Hood and (Maid Marion)
Rogers and (Hammerstein)
Sherlock Holmes and (Dr Watson)
Abbott and (Costello)
Humphrey Bogart and (Lauren Bacall)

**More recent people pairs**
(good for people with dementia born in the 1950s or 1960s)
Simon and (Garfunkel)
Sonny and (Cher)
Tim Rice and (Andrew Lloyd Webber)
Richard Burton and (Elizabeth Taylor)
Torville and (Dean)
Morecombe and (Wise)
Prince Charles and (Princess Diana)
Butch Cassidy and (the Sundance Kid)
French and (Saunders)

## Variations

You can play this game using famous places instead of sayings or pairs. This can provoke discussion about places that people have visited and people's memories of these places.

Some suggestions are offered below, but remember to adapt this game according to the background of the individuals in your group. If you are working with African Caribbean people, for example, research the places that will be familiar to them. If you live in the north of England or in Wales, include popular northern or Welsh locations. Look at local books and tourist information if you are not familiar with the area yourself.

Loch (Ness)
Taj (Mahal)
Eiffel (Tower)
Leaning Tower of (Pisa)
Grand (Canyon)
Niagara (Falls)
Beverley (Hills)
White cliffs of (Dover)
Hampstead (Heath)

Norfolk (broads)
Statue of (Liberty)
Westminster (Abbey)
Trafalgar (Square)
Holy (Island)
Gretna (Green)
Hadrian's (Wall)
Blarney (Stone)
Galway (Bay)

# The beetle game

A version of this game that can be purchased from toyshops uses model beetles, which players put together. However, you can draw a beetle on a piece of paper instead, which demands less manual dexterity and is much cheaper.

People may remember this game from their childhood, in which case you should use the opportunity to reminisce about other childhood games they might have played.

## What is needed

- A Beetle game

or

- Two whiteboards or some flip-chart paper
- Pens
- Two large foam dice

## How it is done

- Divide the group into two teams and give each team one of the dice and either a whiteboard/paper and pen or a Beetle game.

- Each person in the group has a go at throwing the die. When somebody throws a 6, they draw a beetle body (be ready to help, should the person have difficulties drawing). Then a 5 must be thrown, so that the head can be added (see below). The two teams compete to see who can complete their beetle first.
  - When a '6' is thrown, a beetle body is drawn.
  - Then a '5' must be thrown for the head to be drawn.
  - Then a '4' for the legs...
  - Then a '3' for a tail...
  - Then a '2' for the antennae...
  - And finally a '1' for the spots!

Start conversations by asking questions such as, 'Are you afraid of beetles?', 'Are there any other animals or insects that you do not like?', 'Can you draw a beetle?', or, 'Do you have a lucky number?'

**People often recognise numbers on dice more easily if they are written rather than represented by spots. It also helps if you write the number that the group needs on the board/flipchart.**

**Be aware of the cognitive abilities needed to understand the concept of the game and to follow the rules. Different members of the group may be able to do different parts of the activity – for example, throwing the dice or drawing the legs.**

## Variations

You can adapt this game to draw other objects, such as a house ('6' for the outside walls, '5' for the door, '4' for windows, '3' for the roof, '2' for the chimney, '1' for the garden path), an elephant, a car or anything else that people suggest!

# Pass the parcel

## What is needed

- Small prizes, such as chocolate, soap or sweets, to wrap in each layer – alternatively, you could place simple questions in the layers
- A bigger 'star prize' to go inside the final layer of the parcel
- A selection of different papers or fabrics – choose a good range of colours, patterns and textures to introduce a sensory element to the game
- A tape or CD player, a supply of music and somebody to run/stop the music

## How it is done

• Seat everyone in a circle so that they can all see each other. Start the music. Give the parcel to one of the group members and encourage them to pass it on, so that the parcel moves from one person to the next. Stop the music – the person holding the parcel at this moment unwraps the first layer of paper.

• Give the person time to examine and comment on the fabric or paper and to find the small prize hidden in it. If you are playing the game using questions, read the question out and invite an answer from the person holding the parcel. Questions could include, 'What is your favourite

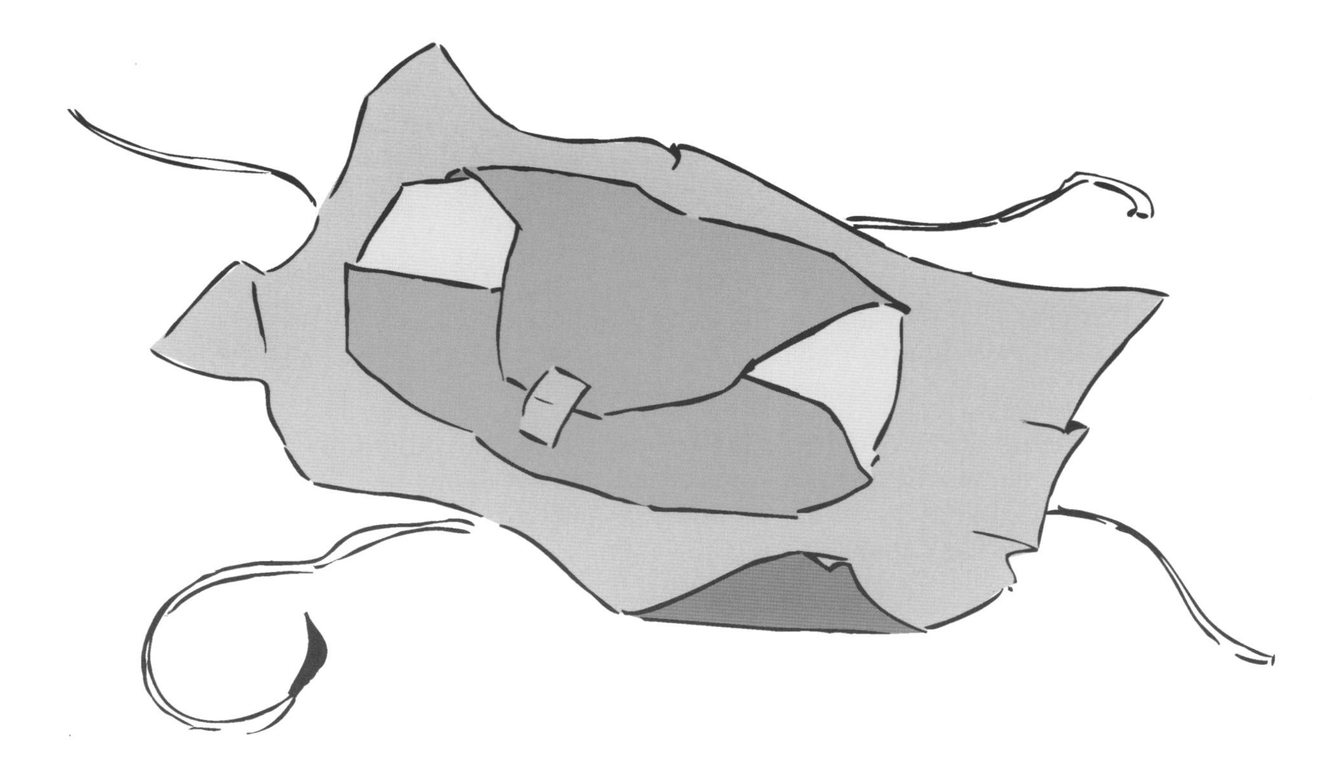

flower?', 'Do you know how to ride a horse?', or, 'If you were going to a party, what colour dress/suit/shirt would you wear?'

- When the person is ready, start the music again and continue passing the parcel until the final wrapping is undone and the prize has been won.

- Try to create a sense of excitement and expectation about passing the parcel on and waiting for the music to stop. Encourage a playful atmosphere – for example, pretend you are about to turn the music off, try to 'steal' one of the prizes or hold on to the parcel yourself.

- You could play different styles of music and encourage the group to pass the parcel quickly to faster music and in 'slow motion' to quieter, slower music. In a more able group, you could also pass the parcel in different moods, for example 'nervously', 'romantically', or 'energetically'.

- Try to start conversations about some of the following topics:
  - Memories of childhood parties
  - People's perfect prizes or presents
  - Surprises that people have enjoyed
  - Likes and dislikes regarding the colours and textures of the wrappings and the sweets and chocolates hidden in them.

**People may hold on to the parcel for a while or seem unsure what to do with it. Try to avoid passing the parcel for people – give everyone plenty of time and encouragement to do it for themselves.**

**Many people will remember this game from childhood parties. This will make it familiar but might make some people feel that it is childish. If it is played with a small child or a group of children, it might be enjoyed most by everyone!**

**If a member of the group is diabetic, ensure that diabetic sweets are included in the wrappings of the parcel and ensure that the right people get these!**

# Body parts

## What is needed

- Two body outlines – one male and one female. Ensure there are enough copies of each to go round the group.
- Pens or crayons
- Books or tables to lean on
- A list of body parts for the activity organiser

## How it is done

• Give each player a body outline – make sure everybody has the same sex outline. You can play the game a second time using the other outline.

• Call out different body parts – for example, the chin, the hips or the nose. Tell players to scribble or mark a cross where they think each body part is on their outline.

• Try using more complex terminology for more able members of the group – for example, 'Where are his biceps?', 'Where is his femur?'

• At the end of the game, go through the body parts you called out and point to where they are on yourself. Alternatively, choose a willing 'model' from the group.

• As you play the game, try to start relevant conversations with the group. Topics might include:
  - Whether people studied biology at school – or were any good at it!
  - Parts of the body people like/dislike about themselves.
  - People's views about other people's bodies – for example, do they like big muscles, small bottoms or blue eyes?
  - What parts of the body would people be most likely to notice first if they are attracted to someone?

**Some people may not be able to draw or hold a pen, but they can usually point to the places mentioned. Some people may draw or doodle on their outline – this is fine!**

**This game is not for the prudish! It will almost certainly encourage those with a naughty sense of humour to mention 'naughty bits' or 'mis-hear' what the organiser says!**

# Beach ball football

## What is needed

- A large, soft blow-up beach ball or a large balloon

## How it is done

- Make sure everybody is seated in chairs in a circle or big square, with the ball in the centre.
- The aim is for players to score goals. A goal is under the chair of another player – everybody is a defender.
- Whoever gets the ball can kick it to anyone else in the group.

**People can slip out of their chairs if they over extend themselves – keep an eye out for this.**

**Wheelchair users may need to have the footplates removed.**

**People who cannot use their legs very easily can use a rolled up newspaper as a 'bat' instead.**

**Some people are nervous of balloons and worry that they are going to burst, especially if they are moved around suddenly.**

# Horse race

## What is needed

- A long plastic sheet or mat. You could use a roll of wallpaper lining, which is cheap and durable as well as easy to roll up and store when not in use. Prepare the mat by drawing up to 20 lines across it width-ways (less if the mat is smaller) so that it is divided into boxes. Number the boxes and write phrases that relate to a horse race in them, such as, 'Horse falls at a jump. Go back five places', 'Jockey whips horse. Move forward two places', or, 'Horse has wind! Move forward one place'.
- One large foam die
- A stick or other long-handled object
- Counters in different colours, or items that represent individual players. If you are feeling creative, you can make cardboard cut-out horses on stands.

## How it is done

- Ask each player to choose a name or number for their horse. Let people be as silly or as serious as they like.
- Each player then takes it in turn to throw the die and move their 'horse' counter forward, following the instructions on whatever space they land on. The winner is the first past the finishing line and could be congratulated with a prize and/or a drink!
- As you play the game, ask people questions such as:
  - Have you ever been to the races? Did you dress up?
  - Do you like gambling? Have you ever won a lot of money?
  - If you did win a large amount (£1,000 / £10,000 / £100,000?) what would you do with it?

**People may not be able to read the instructions on the squares very easily. Make sure that you read them aloud and that everybody has heard and understood them.**

# Music and dance

Photo posed by models

If used well, music and dance can transform the mood of an individual or a group. Upbeat rhythms can raise people's spirits, making them feel more energised and ready to take part in an activity. Relaxing music can support the enjoyment of a massage or a rest after lunch. Marching band music can get people's feet moving for exercise, and a waltz can inspire dancing.

Imagine what your life would be like if you could never listen to music again. You probably listen to music throughout the day, perhaps as you get ready in the morning, as you work during the day, or if you go out shopping or for a meal. Many people are also able to respond to music through dance and enjoy the social interaction that this brings.

Music touches parts of a person that words, intellect and practical pursuits cannot reach. It has been suggested that the ability to hear and respond to music remains long after many other abilities and senses have become very impaired by dementia. Music can be used as a way of communicating and creating trusting relationships with people.

Despite this, in many care settings little attention or investment of money and time is given to using music creatively. Sometimes, the same collection of sing-a-long tunes is played endlessly, or the radio is left on the same music station for hours at a time.

Music should be viewed as a priority area rather than an afterthought in good care practice. Ideally, a member of staff should have specific responsibility for overseeing the provision of music and a budget should be allocated for CDs, tapes, visiting performers and equipment. Have you considered employing a 'musician in residence' to work with your clients or residents on an ongoing basis? This requires a musician with the confidence, skills and qualities to work

EXAMPLE

## Interactive music

An Alzheimer's Society branch describes their involvement in an interactive music project:

'The project's name was 'Sounds from Within Community Music in Mental Health' and it received funding from a grant-giving trust and the local adult and community education department.

'Members of our group were invited to create their own music and lyrics and produce three songs of their choice. With the help of a musical organiser, members of staff, volunteers and various musical instruments, this great challenge was undertaken. It was carried out with enthusiasm and high spirits by all who took part. The final outcome of the project was that all the groups together produced a professional CD. Observing the sense of achievement in the group was a joy for us to watch....

'I have been pleasantly surprised by the various art grants that are available and we have already set about our next venture. I would encourage others to try this route and I hope that you will get as much enjoyment from this as we all did.'

well with people with dementia, to build up relationships and to find ways of using music to communicate with individuals or groups.

Use any resources already available to you. There may be people in the care home or day centre who used to play an instrument; with appropriate support, perhaps they could still play. Do any members of staff, relatives or volunteers have any musical ability that could be used with people with dementia?

Most people with dementia will feel enriched by the interaction and sense of connection that music and dance can offer, so long as emphasis is not placed on doing things 'correctly' but on having fun.

## Recorded music

Here are some ideas for a music collection that could be used by British people predominantly born in the 1920s and 1930s. Why not take some people with dementia with you to a music store and make an activity of exploring the various sections to see which names trigger memories?

- Nostalgia collections from a catalogue, including individual artists such as Peggy Lee, Frank Sinatra and Mario Lanza – this can be an economical way of buying music.
- Mrs Mills or Russ Conway collections – good upbeat, fast, fun piano music, great for lifting a sleepy atmosphere!
- Irish collections – dance music and softer ballads for quieter times
- Scottish dance collections
- English rural dance music – not as well known as Scottish dance music but also very good for getting feet tapping and lifting spirits
- Old time party favourites and pub songs collections – most big stores do these kinds of compilations
- 'They Sold A Million' – four CDs of various artists, including the Ink Spots and Glenn Miller
- 'Great British Dance Bands and Their Vocalists' – a four CD set, including artists such as Al Bowlly, Harry Roy and Nat Gonella
- Strauss waltzes – good for dance and exercise sessions
- Other dance collections – fox trots, military two-steps, twists and barn dance collections
- Traditional band music – good for exercise movements
- Collections from other parts of the world – South American salsa and steel band music from the Caribbean are particularly rhythmical and get people moving. Pan pipes, Indian harps and flutes can be very soothing and soulful.

- Collections from the musicals, such as 'My Fair Lady', 'Me and My Girl' and Gilbert and Sullivan musicals
- Jazz band music
- Collections of opera, ballet and orchestral music – find out which composers or opera singers people enjoy most
- Choral music – many people enjoy listening to Welsh choirs or cathedral choristers
- Music from the 1960s and 1970s such as the Beatles, Neil Diamond, Shirley Bassey, The Carpenters, Simon and Garfunkel, Barbara Streisand and Patsy Cline – many music collections in day centres and care homes are too biased towards the 1930s and 1940s

- Popular children's verses or lullabies are often well remembered by older people and can prompt childhood memories
- People might also enjoy more modern music

EXAMPLE

## Music for Life

Music for Life is an interactive project involving groups of three or four professional musicians, which aims to build new relationships and insights using music improvisation. The project focuses on communication and musicians and staff work together as a team, using a range of verbal and non-verbal approaches to support individuals and the group as a whole. Through voice, a variety of instruments or simply their own bodies, participants are encouraged to 'play' with music, to direct and follow each other and to be aware of and listen to each other.

'Annie, for example, with the expressiveness of her eyes and only minimal hand movements, inspired a deeply moving improvisation supported by the silent, almost tangible focus of the rest of the group. These are moments to be recognised and cherished – when something beyond words or music has been at work and something essentially human and life enhancing has been touched.'

From 'Meeting in the dark – a musical journey of discovery', Linda Rose and Stephanie Schlingensiepen, *Journal of Dementia Care*, Vol 9, issue 2, March/April 2001. Details of Music for Life are included in 'Helpful organisations' on page 154.

## Singing for every day!

If you enjoy using your voice, sing while you go about your business – perhaps while you are dressing and bathing a person. Try to be interactive – voice and touch can go hand in hand. The human voice can be very soothing for a person with dementia. Using a person's name in made up tunes can also be soothing and orientating.

## Dancing for every day!

You can dance throughout the day, not just during specific dance activities! If you feel comfortable using dance spontaneously, include it in your interactions with people with dementia. Here are some ideas:

- Link arms and dance with someone as you invite them to come with you for a meal.
- Serve cakes for tea with an extra flourish of the hands and a bounce in your step.
- Do 'hand jives' on the day centre bus while listening to the radio.
- Do the dusting or the vacuuming with some improvised hand and step movements to different types of music – for example, rock 'n' roll, quiet ballads or band music.

If you give this a try, you will be surprised at how warmly many people with dementia respond and how often they join in!

## Music for every day!

Sitting quietly and listening to music with another person can be very enjoyable and companionable. There is little pressure on either person to communicate verbally and they can benefit from 'just being' together. Be aware of the mood of the music that you choose as this will have an impact on those listening.

# Making sounds and rhythms

## What is needed

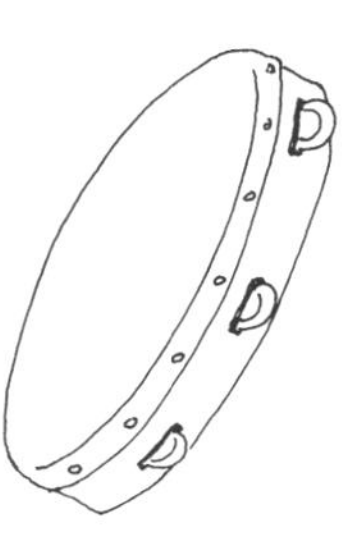

- A selection of instruments, including percussion and small instruments such as castanets, rainmakers, bells and drums
- Jars and tins filled with small items such as buttons, rice or nails so that they make different sounds when shaken
- Cutlery or wooden sticks to knock together or against the jars and tins

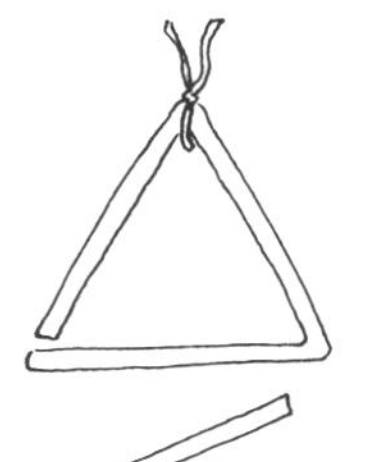

## How it is done

- Encourage people in the group to explore the different instruments and the sounds that they make.
- In groups of two or three, create different rhythms and sounds – slow, fast, soft and loud. Try to make the sounds of different people's footsteps, such a young child's, a soldier's, a ballerina's or an animal's (an elephant, a horse, a mouse or a dolphin, for example).
- Choose four of these different rhythms. Think up some personal details about the characters represented by each of these rhythms and think of what they could be doing. You could go on to create a simple story around the characters you have created, using further sound effects. For example, bells jingling could represent the ballerina falling in love or a drum could sound as the soldier goes to war.

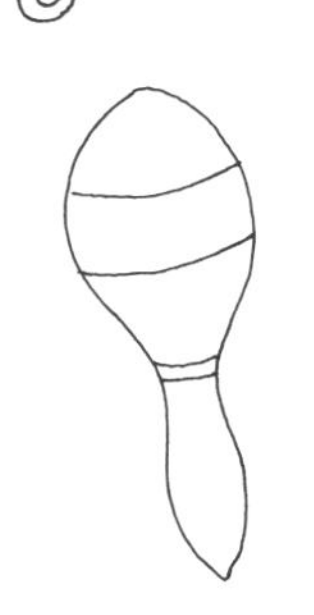

## Variations

Some people might feel confident enough to create sound effects with their voices, their hands or their feet as well as, or instead of, instruments. Think about the noises of the sea, a forest or a busy street on market day and 'play' with the sounds.

**Choose instruments carefully, according to the strength and ability of different people. Some instruments need more arm, finger and hand co-ordination than others. People may quickly get frustrated if they cannot produce any sound from their instrument or find it awkward or heavy to hold.**

**Check the quality of sound and the finish of instruments. Some cheaper instruments may be tempting but not robust enough to cope with frequent use in a dementia setting. Sharp edges or rough surfaces can cause problems.**

**Don't patronise people with instruments that are obviously intended for young children or 'toy' instruments.**

Adapted with permission from *Creative groupwork with elderly people: drama*, Madeline Andersen-Warren, 1996, Speechmark Publishing Ltd, Bicester

# A sing-along activity

## What is needed

- Copied song sheets in large print may be helpful
- A piano and guitar (and people who can play them) are ideal but not essential
- Small percussion instruments – to be used by people who prefer to participate with their hands rather than their voices

## How it is done

- There are many different ways of encouraging people to sing. Sometimes, you only need to suggest a song and individuals will start singing it with you. Singing can be particularly beneficial for people in the more advanced stages of dementia. Give them time to participate in their own way, perhaps through moving their lips, tapping their feet or squeezing your hand.
- Give people choice and control. Let them start a song or request a personal favourite.
- Divide songs into themes – for example, songs about nature, food or love, or songs linked to names (although you will need to do some 'homework' for this in case people get stuck!) One Alzheimer's Society branch suggested using visual props relevant to the music, such as military uniforms for songs about the army or police hats for the 'Gendarmes' duet'.
- Always encourage and celebrate spontaneity and choice – if a person suddenly starts a new song, follow their lead and sing with them. If the group wishes to sing the same song again and again, go along with them. If people get up and dance, enjoy this. If a song prompts a personal story or memory, give the person time to share it.

**Song sheets can be confusing or distracting for some people, and can cause anxiety or a sense of pressure. People often remember the words spontaneously in any case! Song sheets might, however, help members of staff offer prompts if needed.**

**People who were not brought up in Britain could feel excluded when people remember and join in songs they have never heard. Ask the person's relatives about songs they may remember. People may be able to teach other members of the group a simple song from their own country.**

**Younger people with dementia will remember different songs to an older client group.**

### Variations

**Guess the name of the song**

The pianist or guitarist plays a fragment from a piece and asks people to guess what it is. If you do not have a musical instrument, you could hum a piece instead. There is a wonderful sense of delight and achievement when people get it right!

## Guess the song title

### What is needed

- Prepared word cards – pick a song title, such as 'Night and Day', 'Show Me the Way to go Home' or 'I'm Getting Married in the Morning' and write one word from the title on each card, for example, 'Getting', 'Married' and 'Morning'.

### How it is done

- Shuffle the cards. Show one card to the group and ask them to think of a song that has that word in it. Ask them to hum or sing it – this often gets people going!
- If nobody can think of a song for the first word card, hold up a second card as the next clue and continue until the song is guessed.

**Not everybody likes to sing or be put on the spot. Be aware of any signs of discomfort.**

With thanks to Colin Harrison, volunteer co-ordinator, Newfield House, ExtraCare Charitable Trust

# A hymn, a thought and a prayer

This is an example of a weekly service run for people in a dementia care home that does not rely on a visiting minister. The organiser who devised this service used his previous experience as a church organist to create a format that would bring together familiar rituals and a range of well-loved music. The service lasts only half an hour.

The range of music suggested here should inspire you to choose some of your own favourites. Combine joyful and celebratory pieces with quieter and more reflective ones. People with dementia often respond particularly well to these changes in mood and they provide a focus for attention and group unity.

## What is needed

- Someone who has the confidence and commitment to lead a service on a regular basis. This does not have to be a religious minister, but it does need to be someone with a Christian faith, some charismatic group leadership qualities and a fundamental belief in the importance of sustaining people's spiritual lives.
- It is best to have a pianist or organist to provide live music, but if this is not possible, use taped music instead.

## How it is done

• Arrange the room so that there is a table with a tablecloth and fresh flowers on it at the front. You could place a laminated card with a picture of a church window and the words 'A Hymn, a Thought and a Prayer' on the table. Add anything else that you like. Set out chairs in semi-circles, or however you feel is appropriate.

• If you have a pianist, they should play music as people enter the room and sit down. The person leading the service can stand at the front of the room by the table.

• The introductory pieces of music create a calm and welcoming atmosphere as well as acting as a cue for people with dementia that the service is about to begin. Here are some pieces you could use:

– 'Greensleaves'
– 'Jesu joy'
– 'Drink to me only with thine eyes' (an English Air)
– 'Londonderry air'

• Once everyone is seated, hand out large-print hymn sheets.

• You could start the service with 'Praise My Soul, the King of Heaven'. In the home where this service was created, everyone tried to stand up to the opening bars of the hymn, as they would have done

*Greensleeves*

Alas my love you do me wrong
To cast me off discourteously;
And I have loved you oh so long
Delighting in your company.

Greensleeves was my delight,
Greensleeves my heart of gold
Greensleeves was my heart of joy
And who but my Lady Greensleeves.

I have been ready at your hand
To grant whatever thou would'st crave;
I have waged both life and land
Your love and goodwill for to have.

Greensleeves was my delight,
Greensleeves my heart of gold
Greensleeves was my heart of joy
And who but my Lady Greensleeves.

when they attended church. The repetition of the refrain, 'Praise Him, praise Him' was particularly appreciated by the congregation.

- Next, read a short poem or a prayer. Extracts from books such as the *Lion's treasury of children's prayers* can be useful as they are simply and clearly written.

- Then, sing together three verses of 'Morning has Broken', and then listen to a soothing and peaceful piece of music, such as 'In a Monastery Garden' by Albert Ketelbey.

- Offer another poem or prayer.

- Next, try singing a popular and well-known hymn, such as 'All Things Bright and Beautiful' – people tend to sing this one with great gusto!

- The service leader then invites people to think about going on a journey, saying words such as:

  > *'It's about time we went for a sail. Let's imagine we're on a sailing yacht or maybe on a trip on the canal down the road (mention local rivers/canals/sea that may be remembered by the group). We could even be enjoying a glass of wine or a gin and tonic on a big ship or liner.'*

- Play an orchestral version of 'I am sailing' at this point. Many people will close their eyes and stay very quiet and still as they are transported on their inner 'journey'.

- Finally, hand out large-print copies of the 'Lord's prayer', and read it together.

- A number of closing pieces can be played on the piano, such as:
  - 'Lord of the Dance' by Sydney Carter
  - 'Sing Hosanna' by A Sevison

- Encourage everyone to clap to the rhythm and to applaud at the end of the service. People with dementia are in this way encouraged to spontaneously express themselves, rather than being bound by the conventions of an ordinary church service.

- As people leave, try to sustain the uplifting atmosphere with an upbeat piece of music, such as 'Kensington High Street' by Eric Coates.

**Not everyone will find participation in Christian rituals a source of enjoyment or comfort, so do not try to make people attend. Carefully observe how people respond to the service. However, even if someone was not a regular church-goer earlier in their life, they may still benefit from the opportunity to participate in a service like this. The combination of time spent with others singing songs and quieter moments of listening and spirituality can affect those who would not necessarily describe themselves as religious.**

# Dance as a key to contact and communication

**Dancing can be a way for a person with dementia to express themselves in a more intuitive way and when words are hard to find.**

EXAMPLE

Miss Daisy Lane is an 88-year-old woman who seems very reserved and solitary. She rarely talks to other members of the day centre and often becomes upset and agitated when members of staff try to help her with any personal care. She lives on her own and very little is known about her past.

One afternoon, some waltzes are being played on the music centre. Rajni, a care worker, approaches Miss Lane, who is sitting looking sad in a corner of the room, and politely invites her to dance, although she half expects her to refuse. Miss Lane stands up and takes Rajni's hand a little hesitantly at first. As she starts to move, a gradual transformation takes place in her face and movements. Her feet start to step sideways, backwards and forwards in time to the music, her body sways and she lifts Rajni's hand up high and does a graceful and spontaneous turn under her arm.

Her eyes sparkle and she laughs with delight as Rajni responds by doing a similar turn under her arm. They clasp hands tightly and enjoy a moment of close eye contact and emotional connection as the waltz comes to an end.

Miss Lane suddenly says, with great feeling and clarity, 'I never did much dancing as a child'. She then starts to tell Rajni about her childhood in a Barnado's children's home and how she had always longed to run away and be a dancer. It is as if the music and the movement had made Miss Lane feel safe enough to share this account of her difficult past. She tells Rajni, 'You can call me Daisy!', and says that she would like to dance every day, 'to make up for lost time!'

# Circle dancing

## What is needed

- If possible, a piano and somebody able to play it. Otherwise, a collection of music and a stereo system. Songs that have actions in them, such as the 'Hokey Cokey', are particularly good.
- Optional – scarves, ribbons or canes.

## How it is done

- Form a large circle around the room, with everybody facing inwards. Ensure that all chairs, tables and any other objects are all safely pushed to the edges of the room. People in wheelchairs can also participate, so long as a staff member is able to push them.
- Play some music. Designate one member of staff to call out and demonstrate the actions that the participants should make, for example, 'Clap your hands!', or, 'Shout hooray!' Everybody in the circle should copy the leader so that everybody is dancing together. It is a good idea for everyone to hold hands so that people don't wander off in the wrong direction – although if people don't want to hold hands, this is fine.

## Variations

Use colourful scarves, ribbons or canes as props. These can be swirled in the air to great effect or tapped on the floor in time to the music.

## Circle dancing in practice

Dorothy Jerrome, who runs circle dancing classes in Brighton, explains how effective the classes are in providing stimulating activity for people with dementia:

'Each session lasted an hour during which we danced about eight dances. The dances come from around the world. The dance steps were adapted for this group – walks, sways, slip-steps, rocking – with simplified rhythms.

'Circle dancing is a way of communicating through touch and rhythm. The circling and holding, the rocking and gentle repetitive movements, communicate acceptance directly and without words ... The music touches something deep within the person. The circle is a social situation. The dancers make reference to each other, to the non-dancers sitting watching, and to the shared dances ... The most minimal of movements such as gentle swaying from foot to foot, is a means of finding physical balance. In people with dementia, this focusing on one's centre might help support the fragile inner balance which in the early stages people fight to retain.

'To assist with balance and communicate the rhythm to the more impaired people I tend to use a close arm hold (locking elbows). A shoulder hold in the Greek dances has the same effect.

'I put on a tape and dance a bit myself before inviting them to join in.

'Some encounters are very moving, as when Edward persuaded Mary to join the circle. Newly arrived for respite care, Mary was shy and nervous, refusing all invitations to dance. Edward, a gentle and courteous man at an advanced stage of the disease, offered his hand and waited until Mary rose to her feet. Kissing her on the cheek he told her, 'You are a lovely girl!' with a tenderness and respect perhaps once reserved for his wife or daughter.

Extracts from 'Circles of the Mind' by Dorothy Jerrome, *Journal of Dementia Care*, May/June 1999

# Movement and drama

The world of 'make believe' and fantasy can provide people with freedom of self expression. People often feel less pressured in an atmosphere of make believe than in other social situations. The emphasis in drama on non-verbal expression can also empower a person with dementia and help them to communicate their feelings

Drama offers a variety of opportunities for people to move and to benefit from exercise without feeling that they are doing hard work. People are often more likely to pretend to hang out the washing or to ride a bicycle than they are to put their arms in the air or move their legs in an exercise class.

Care workers, however, often lack confidence in leading dramatic activities. More extrovert people, or people with a background in acting or dancing, might be more prepared to do this.

Activities for different levels of abilities are included here. For people with more advanced dementia, the emphasis should be less on 'acting' (this demands high cognitive abilities) and more on play, movement and engagement of the senses.

**This type of activity is not for everybody. A person should always be able to just watch. If a person seems to be uncomfortable or awkward in the group, do not make them take part.**

**Some dramatic activities can seem childish or silly to a person with dementia. People in the early stages of their illness, in particular, might feel anxious about making a fool of themselves and resist taking part. You will need skill and sensitivity in order to create a playful atmosphere that also feels safe enough for people to join in.**

**If a person with dementia is also experiencing either psychotic or neurotic symptoms, activities involving drama should be avoided unless a qualified dramatherapist is involved. Drama plays with different versions of reality, and this could provoke extreme reactions from a person who is experiencing mental distress.**

Adapted with permission from *Creative groupwork with elderly people: drama*, Madeline Andersen-Warren, 1996, Speechmark Publishing Ltd, Bicester

# Cushions exercise

This is a warm-up exercise that uses movements of the hands, arms and shoulders and introduces an atmosphere of 'make-believe'.

## What is needed:

- Soft, light cushions or pillows

## How it is done

- Position group members so that they are sitting in a big circle facing each other and give each person a cushion or pillow to hold on their lap. Tell everyone to put their hands on the cushion and knead it gently. Then ask them to act out the following:

  – that they are cats clawing at the cushion

  – that they are embroidering a pattern onto the cover of the cushion, threading the needle slowly and sewing with small, neat stitches

  – that the cushion is a piece of dough that they are kneading

  – that the cushion is a soft animal going to sleep and that they are stroking it

Ask what else the cushion could 'be' and mime some suggestions. Ask whether anyone has craft hobbies or interests that they could mime in a similar way.

Then tell everyone to shake their hands and relax.

# Waiting at the bus stop

Adapted with permission from 'Creative Groupwork with Elderly People: Drama', Madeline Andersen-Warren, 1996, Speechmark Publishing Ltd, Bicester

This warm-up activity uses the head, trunk, hands and arms and is good for flexibility.

## How it is done

- Ask group members to sit or stand in a row, all facing in the same direction. Ask them to move their head slowly to the right and then to the left. Repeat twice. Then ask them to move their right arm to the front, then their left arm. Repeat twice.
- Now ask everyone to act out the following (you can demonstrate):
  - You are all in a bus queue. Which end is the front of the queue?
  - Look into the distance to see if the bus is coming. You may need to move to the left or right to see past those in front of you.
  - Look at your watches. You are annoyed because the bus is always late. Shake your heads and look at your watches again.
  - The bus is coming. Watch it come nearer. What number bus is it? It does not look as if it will stop. Put out your arms to signal it to stop. It is full. Shrug your shoulders as the bus goes past.
  - It is getting cold. Rub your arms and shoulders.
  - The next bus comes. Put your arms out to stop it.
  - Relax in relief as the bus stops.
- Use this exercise to start conversations. You could ask people what number buses they remember using and what route they took. If they were getting on a bus now, what would be their favourite destination?

## Variations

Try creating different kinds of queues – for example, a post office queue or a supermarket checkout queue. Act out conversations between the waiting people. Create a situation where one person (possibly a member of staff) jumps the queue and encourage some responses.

**Be aware that a group needs to feel very safe to deal with situations of potential frustration like this, even if improvised in a fun way. You must be able to deal with expressions of anger or distress if participants get too involved in the improvisation.**

# The hats game

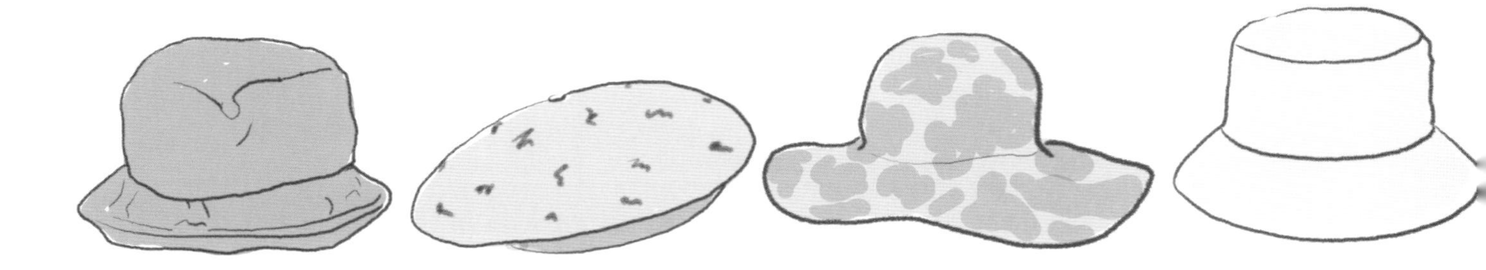

## What is needed

- A good selection of hats or wigs, collected from charity shops, party shops, children's shops or from relatives and friends. You need at least one hat or wig for every participant. You could get, for example, wedding hats, Easter bonnets, police officer hats, fireman hats, jester hats, witch hats, bowler hats, top hats, French berets, sea captain hats or army officer hats.
- A portable mirror – if people are trying hats on, they must be able to see what they look like. Be aware that some people with dementia might not recognise themselves in a mirror.

## How it is done:

- Sit in a circle of chairs or round a large table and place the collection of hats in the centre of the group. Encourage people to pick up individual hats and comment on them.

- Invite people to choose and try on a hat that appeals to them in some way – possibly because they think it is funny or because it reminds them of someone or something. You should also try on a hat and ask for comments; 'Does it suit me?', 'Where might I wear this one?' etc.

- When everyone who wants to has put on a hat of their choice, invite them to look at themselves in the mirror. Ask everyone to give themselves a name to fit the character who would wear their hat. If people struggle with this, other group members might offer possibilities. Be positive about all suggestions that are offered, however bizarre they might seem. Can people think of a gesture that this person might make – for example, a salute for an army officer, or a 'royal wave' for someone wearing a Queen's hat?

If people are independently mobile, they could stand up and walk around the circle, greeting and shaking hands with other characters. A group dance is another possibility and can result in some amusing dance couples, such as a witch and a police officer, or a princess and a jester. At the end of the activity session, let people take their hats off themselves and say 'goodbye' to the character they have been playing.

**Some people hate wearing hats or having their heads covered. Make sure that you have clear permission from a person before you put a hat on them.**

**Be careful about laughing at a person who looks particularly silly in their hat. People who are feeling vulnerable might feel exposed and distressed in this situation.**

EXAMPLE

## The hats game in practice

Albert was offered a policeman's hat to try on, which he did with a solemn expression on his face, immediately assuming the posture of a 'bobby' with his legs slightly apart and knees bent. Carol, the care worker came up to him and said, 'Help me officer, someone has stolen my wallet'. Thora, who was sitting quietly in a chair watching, without any prompting from staff suddenly grabbed her frame and pretended to make an escape saying, 'I didn't do it Officer, I promise I didn't do it!' and with a cheeky grin on her face, winked at Carol.

# The magic carpet

This exercise demands quite a high level of concentration and conceptual understanding, and will probably only work well with people in the earlier stages of dementia. However, people in the later stages of dementia may enjoy the visual and tactile experience of holding the 'carpet' and listening to other people talking. You will need a group of people who are reasonably relaxed and used to being together, and a skilled group leader.

## What is needed

- A large colourful blanket, cloth or light carpet
- Optional items that you could use are a map of the UK, a map of the world, a large globe or a passport.

## How it is done

- Introduce the idea of a magic carpet – a carpet that can take people to any place in the world immediately. You could say, 'Wouldn't it be wonderful if you could just sit on a magic carpet, shut your eyes and be transported somewhere else in an instant?'
- Then lay your cloth or carpet on the ground in the centre of the group. Encourage people to comment on its size, shape and colour.
- Ask group members to shut their eyes and think about a beautiful place that they would like to visit. Perhaps you could say the following words very slowly, leaving pauses between each question so that people can think about their answers. You may want to play some music to help with the following 'guided fantasy'.

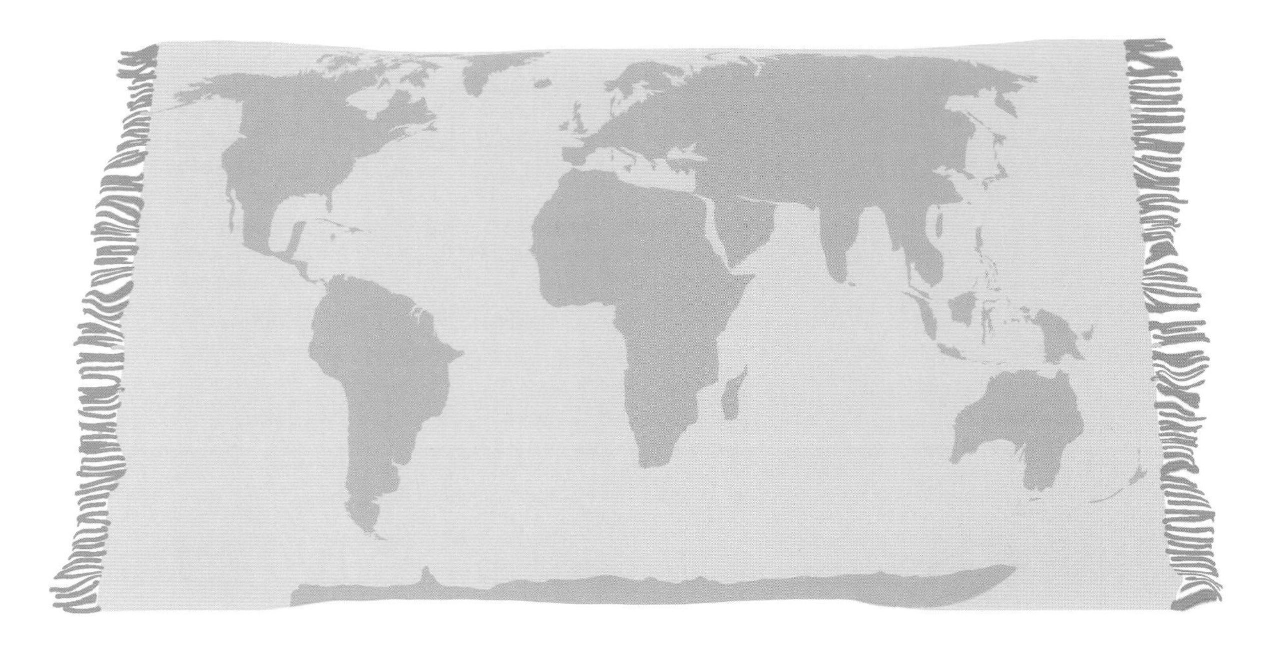

*'If you had a choice of anywhere in the world to visit on your own magic carpet, where would it be? It might be just down the road from here, or it might be thousands of miles away... It is a place that you would really love to visit... You may have been there before or it may be a place in your imagination...*

*What is the weather like in this place? What colour is the sky? Do you feel hot or cold? Is it in Britain or is it abroad? Is it in the countryside or a town? Is it by the sea or in the mountains? Are there any people? Are there any animals or trees or flowers? What are the sounds you might hear in this place? What are the colours? Are there any smells? What feelings do you have when you are in this place? Are you sitting somewhere or are you perhaps walking or floating around? Take time to enjoy being in this place...*

*In a few moments, you will be opening your eyes to come back into the room again, but don't rush. You may feel like you have travelled somewhere in your mind. Hold on to some of the pictures, sounds and smells in your head. Take your time. Now open your eyes slowly and look around at the other people in the group, who have been on other journeys. I wonder where we have all been in our minds?'*

- Ask people how they found the experience. Some may have drifted off, some may have struggled to concentrate, but others may have thought of particular places.

- Lift up the cloth or carpet and help everyone in the group to hold on to it together.

- Ask someone who seems to have enjoyed the activity to share their magic carpet destination with the group. If nobody wants to do this, a member of staff who has participated can share their ideal location. Ask the person some of the following questions:
  - Have you ever been there before?
  - What makes the place special to you?
  - How would you travel there?
  - Who, if anyone, would you take with you?
  - Tell us what it is like there...

- Put the carpet back down on the ground when the person has finished sharing their experience and lift it up again if someone else wants to describe their 'journey'.

- Acknowledge the different places that you have talked about, looking at where they are on the map if this is helpful.

- At the end of the session, try to ground people back in the here and now. Comment on the town or county you are in and on the real weather outside. Try to think of something positive about your location so that the group don't feel too flat about coming back to 'reality.'

# Actions charades

Many older people are familiar with charades and will grasp the concept of the game quickly. You need small teams of people and a care worker who has played charades before and/or is confident using drama. Charades places very little emphasis on verbal fluency, enabling many people with dementia to play.

## How it is done

- The object of the game is to mime actions, without using words, for the other team(s) to guess. Demonstrate the game first by miming an action such as pouring a cup of tea or riding a horse. Ask participants to guess what you are doing.

- You can write out some suitable actions on pieces of card and give them out to the teams. These might include:
  - A bar man serving drinks
  - A secretary typing a letter
  - A violinist in an orchestra
  - A person doing the ironing, vacuuming or polishing
  - A bus conductor giving out a ticket
  - A person taking their dog for a walk
  - A person arranging flowers or doing the gardening
  - A nurse taking someone's pulse
  - A film star giving someone his/her autograph
  - A cowboy lassoing an animal
  - A garden gnome fishing in a pond!

- Let each team have a few moments to practise before 'performing' for the other team(s). One person in the team can be chosen to act each time, or the team may want to make a joint effort.

**All of these actions can be adapted for people who are not independently mobile and use a wheelchair. A cowboy can lasso sitting down as well as standing up!**

# Improvised situations

This is a more advanced version of action charades, in which people take on a role in a particular situation. Choose situations that will be familiar to members of the group.

## How it is done

- Demonstrate how to play the game clearly, so that people can follow your example. If you act out one of the scenes first, you can then encourage people to become involved.
- Offer people a choice of parts to play and explain the situation that they are going to act out clearly and simply.
- Here are some examples of situations that you could act out:
  - A customer complaining to a shopkeeper about something they have bought – for example, a dress that has shrunk or food that was stale.
  - A family on a beach; the children want ice creams and the parents are trying to sleep in the sun.
  - A doctor's waiting room, where all the patients are trying to get to the front of the queue because of their particular illness: a sore stomach, a flu bug, a sick child. The receptionist is tired and fed up and wants to go home.
  - A police officer who has caught a thief stealing someone's handbag.
  - A pop group playing their first concert together. Carefully choose who is playing what instrument and who is the lead singer. Give the group a name. As one 92 year old woman said, 'We're not the Beatles, we're more like the Snails!'

**Never push a person if they struggle getting into the role or the situation.**

**It is important to have a closing exercise that allows people to step out of the role that they have been playing and to return to being themselves. People may want to reflect on what it was like to act out a role – this will depend on their level of cognitive impairment. You could sing a familiar song, or do a dance, as a closing exercise for people with less verbal ability. If you have used props such as hats or clothing, make a ritual of removing the items and returning them to a box.**

Adapted with permission from *Creative groupwork with elderly people: drama*, Madeline Andersen-Warren, 1996, Speechmark Publishing Ltd, Bicester

# Creating a story from a picture

## What is needed

A selection of postcards or pictures that show people engaged in different activities. Old pictures or photographs from a local library archive or a local history book can be particularly stimulating as they might relate to a period which is more familiar to people in the group. Try to choose different settings – for example, people at a railway station, a dance or a picnic in the countryside.

## How it is done

- Choose a picture and show it to the people in the group.

- Ask the following questions, taking time to listen to the answers and to repeat suggestions that people contribute. This repetition is important as it helps to hold people's interest and can sometimes encourage people to elaborate the story farther. You should gradually build up a story.
  - Where do you think these people are?
  - Who are they? What is their relationship? Are they friends or relatives?
  - Why are they there?
  - What are they doing?
  - When is this scene taking place (day, year, season)
  - Is it a happy occasion or a difficult situation?
  - What do you think they might be saying to each other?
  - What do you think might happen next?

Photograph reproduced with kind permission from Magic Lantern Gems

- Some people will contribute more than others. People may find it easier to respond if you offer one or two suggestions, rather than asking open questions. For example, rather than saying, 'Who are these two people?', you could say, 'Do you think he is her brother or her fiancé?'

- At the end of the session, show the picture to everybody again and repeat the final version of the story. Thank everyone for helping to create the story.

## Variations

If you are working with people who are used to creating these picture stories, you could try using pictures from children's books and creating a children's story. This sometimes allows more opportunities for fantasy, stereotypical 'goodies' and 'baddies', and fairy tale endings.

# Themed exercise sessions

Describing particular actions for people to mime can motivate them to move much more effectively than simply asking them to exercise different parts of their bodies.

## What is needed

- A selection of props might be useful. These could include clothes, balls, carnival sticks and balloons.
- A selection of lively music to inspire people and get them moving.

## How it is done

- Call out a theme from the list provided below and then ask people to mime particular actions. It will be easier if you stand in full sight of everybody and demonstrate the mime, so that people can copy you. People should sit in upright chairs rather than soft comfortable chairs when doing any kind of exercise.
- People may move their arms more if you encourage them to dance holding carnival sticks or brightly coloured cloths. Using a balloon or ball can prompt people to move their feet so that they can kick it away.
- Here are some ideas for actions to mime:

**Housework**
- Wringing clothes dry
- Hanging clothes out to dry on the washing line
- Doing the ironing
- Folding clothes

**The orchestra**
- Conducting the orchestra with your arms in the air
- Playing the violin
- Playing the saxophone
- Crashing a large pair of symbols together

**Other ideas**
- Dipping your feet in the water to see how cold it is
- Rowing a boat
- Pedalling a bicycle – lift your feet up as you go down the hill!
- Waking up in the morning, stretching and yawning
- Rubbing your hands to get warm by a fire

**Staff leading exercise sessions must be adequately trained and insured, and must carry out appropriate individual assessments. For this reason, no specific exercise routines are suggested here. Books with more detailed information about exercise and older people are listed in 'Useful publications and resources' on page 157.**

# Arts and crafts

Sunflower picture reproduced with permission from Christine Bleathman and Murray House Mental Health Resource Unit

Some people find it difficult to participate in creative activities. This is often because they have been told at some point in their life that they are no good at art. However, experience with people with dementia has proved that involvement in artistic activities can enhance a person's confidence and provide opportunities for self-expression.

The dilemma for a person facilitating an art group is how much to 'push' a person to take part. It is important to respect a person's choice not to get involved in an activity, but sometimes you can get past the initial 'block' and give the person the opportunity to enjoy being absorbed in a creative pursuit.

Engagement in the creative process can be demonstrated in quite unusual ways, and sometimes through behaviour that carers or care workers think is 'difficult'. It is important that people are able to express their creativity in whichever ways they choose.

EXAMPLE

## Creative self-expression

Mrs Jones spent up to 20 minutes each morning carefully shredding her paper serviette into small pieces and then arranging them in piles and patterns on the table. She seemed totally absorbed and content whilst involved with this activity and always seemed proud of her finished creation.

The process of participating is the important part, not the end product. There are many different ways of participating, including picking up and touching the art materials, choosing a colour or a pattern or watching others at work.

### Other ideas not covered in this chapter

Only a limited number of activities can be given in this chapter, but there are many more that are suitable for work with people who have dementia. Here are some further examples:

- **Adult colouring books** – be very careful how these are used, as they can be degrading to some people.
- **Stencils** – you can buy these from art shops or make your own.
- **Knitting squares, scarves etc** – most people over 60 are considerably better at knitting than most people under 40!
- **Patchwork quilt making**, using spare cuts of fabrics.
- **Rug making** – kits are available, but be aware that this might be a difficult new skill to learn if people have not tried it before.
- **Plaster of paris moulds for modelling** – kits are available.

The peacock activity by Marlene Rolfe

# The peacock

This is a wonderful 'failure free' group activity, which produces a very pleasing end result, and uses plenty of group interaction. If you can afford to, invest in the acrylic paints – the colours are very strong and attractive, and if used carefully the bottles last a long time.

## What is needed

- A selection of paint brushes
- Pencils
- Paper plates (to use as palettes) or six palette dishes for poster paints to be mixed in
- Old jam jars (for water)
- One large sheet of paper or card
- An assorted mix of A4 coloured and plain white paper or card
- A good range of System 3 acrylic paints (ideally at least six colours) available from a catalogue or art shop – alternatively, use poster paints pre-mixed with water in a palette
- Plastic tablecloth or enough newspaper to cover table
- Enough pairs of scissors to go round

## How it is done

- Prepare paper plates as palettes (one for each person in the group) with a small squeeze of each colour round the edge (if you are using acrylics). If you are using poster paints, hand out palette dishes containing the pre-mixed paints. Also make sure each person has a pencil and a brush or brushes and easy access to a jar of water.
- Ask everyone to draw around their hand; help anybody who has difficulty doing this. Every member of staff should also draw round their own hand so that everyone is involved in the experience.
- Encourage everyone to colour in their handprint with any colours or patterns that they like. There is no right or wrong way of doing this – it is only important to cover all of the handprint in paint.
- Now cut out the handprints. Some people with dementia will have no difficulty with this, but others may need a worker to do it with or for them.
- Whilst the hand shapes are drying, ask group member how they found the activity: was it better or worse than they had expected? Did

it remind of them school, and, if so, what memories of school did they have?

• Put the large sheet of paper or card on the table, and either draw (if you are a confident drawer) or bring out a ready prepared picture of the body and head of a peacock. Arrange all the different hands on the peacock's body to represent the fanned out feathers.

• When everyone is happy with how the hands are arranged, stick them on to the card. The final effect is usually very colourful and attractive.

**If you are working with a mixed ability group, be aware that some people will finish painting or cutting out much more quickly than others; you will need to hold the interest of the whole group by prompting conversation or doing some clearing up.**

## Variations

If possible, involve some children in this activity – children as young as 4 or 5 will enjoy it. The different sizes of hands also create a pleasing effect!

Try using footprints instead of handprints or creating a hedgehog or porcupine for the finished picture.

# Salt dough making

This is a simple and inexpensive activity. Some people with dementia might mistake it for a cooking session, since it uses flour and water. Although this might be confusing for some, it can also provoke conversation and humour. The moulding of the mixture is very tactile and totally safe – the materials are harmless if fingers get licked. The moulding of objects gives opportunities for individual choice and self-expression.

This activity ideally involves three separate sessions:

**First session** – making the dough, moulding the object and baking it.

**Second session** – painting the object.

**Third session** – varnishing the object.

## What is needed

- 200g (7oz) flour
- 100g (3.5oz) salt
- 100ml (3.5fl oz) water
- 1 tablespoon vegetable oil
- Paints
- Paintbrushes
- Varnish – or you can use non-toxic PVA glue
- Latex gloves
- Baking trays
- Mixing bowls

## How it is done

### Session 1 – making the dough and doing the modelling

- Take some people with dementia out shopping with you to get the ingredients, if possible.

- Measure out the flour, water and salt. Group members can help do this. Large old-fashioned scales are best because they are familiar to people and easy to read.

- Mix the flour and salt together in a mixing bowl. Gradually add the water until you have a firm dough. Finally, add the vegetable oil and knead the dough until it is easy to mould. Involve members of the group in this process.

- Give each person in the group a portion of dough and encourage them to make something with it. You can use an example, although sometimes everyone will copy this! Use magazines with pictures of animals, flowers, pots and boxes in them to help stimulate ideas.

Create an atmosphere of 'anything goes'. People can create abstract shapes that do not resemble anything in particular.

- When everyone has finished their object, explain that the objects have to be baked to make them hard. Bake the objects at 180°C or gas mark 4 for a couple of hours, or until they are hard. If health and safety considerations permit and you have an accessible kitchen, involve members of the group in taking the objects to the oven and collecting them when they are ready.

**Session 2 – painting**

- Display the objects on a table so that people can admire their creations.

- Make sure you have a good range of paintbrush sizes. Some people will enjoy doing quite detailed painting and will take a long time with it. Others might only use one colour and find it easier to use a larger brush.

- Encourage everyone to paint their object with any colours or designs that they choose. It might help if you hold the object while the person paints it.

**Session 3 – varnishing**

- Varnishing can be a messy job; again, it is sometimes best to work in pairs, with one person holding and turning the object, and the other person painting on the varnish. You may want to use gloves for this.

- The varnishing will not take long. Make the most of this final session by celebrating the achievement of the group and the individual contributions. Discuss what people would like to do with their finished creation.

**People may be negative about their finished creation, and say that they don't think it is any 'good'. Be sensitive to this kind of reaction; to simply say, 'Well, I think it is lovely!' can be seen as patronising or dismissive of the person's feelings. Sometimes it is better to acknowledge feelings of dissatisfaction by saying something like, 'Sometimes it is hard when things don't turn out as well as we hope', or, 'Is there anything you might do differently if you did it again?'**

**If time passes between the sessions, some people may have no memory of their work. Be careful how you remind them; you might make a person feel either silly or irritated if you insist they made something that they are sure they have never seen before.**

# A colour theme discussion

## What is needed

- A collection of objects that are all the same colour. You can use food, flowers, tools, items of clothing and so on.

## How it is done

- Display all of your chosen objects on a table. Make the display look as attractive and interesting as possible. You can ask group members to contribute objects to the display if they wish.

- Ask people what they think about the objects. Do they like the colour? Do the objects remind them of anything? Take one object at a time and invite conversation about any associations that people may have with it. Only discuss as many items as interest and concentration allows. Be flexible and don't worry if the conversation appears to be going off at a tangent. The effect of the total display adds to the sensory experience.

**Be prepared for somebody to say that they don't like the colour at all. Acknowledge this as a valid response.**

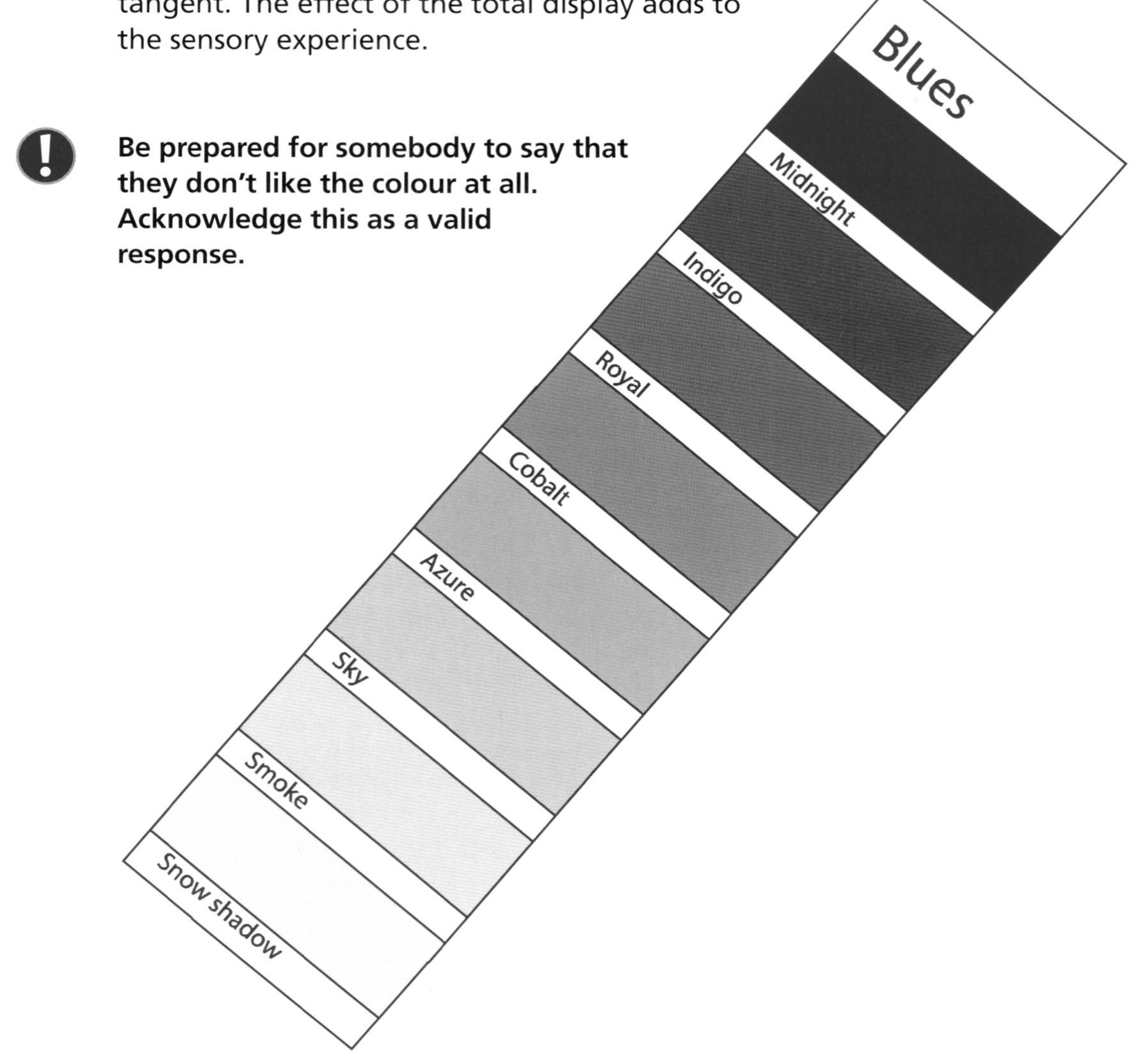

# Creating a fantasy character

For this activity to be successful, you need to create a playful atmosphere that encourages people to use their imagination and contribute their ideas freely.

## What is needed

- A bag of odds and ends – ribbons, feathers, bells, buttons, jewellery, silk flowers, shells, driftwood, wooden spoons, empty chocolate boxes, paper clips, pasta shapes and so on!
- Felt-tipped pens
- A glue stick
- Staples
- Poster board or heavy cardboard

## How it is done

- Choose one fairly large object, such as a piece of driftwood, which is an interesting shape.
- Begin the session by asking, 'What does this look like?' Any answer is a good one! Respond positively to every suggestion. Place a few other articles from your 'goodie bag' around, as you talk about creating a make-believe character or object. Start to put some of the objects together and think of what they could represent; for example, ribbons could be hair, flowers could be eyes, and feathers could be legs. Encourage everyone to add to the creation.
- Give any characters or objects that you invent names or functions. For example, you could create a newly married couple called Bert and Betty, a Loch Ness Monster who is frightened of everybody, or Percy the Parrot who never stops talking. Make up stories about them with the group.

**People may initially find this activity silly and abstract. However, they may still enjoy looking at some of the objects, and may 'warm up' to the fantasy element as some of the characters emerge.**

## Variations

This can be a very good activity to do with children, as they can encourage the adults to enter the fantasy world.

# Your version of an old master

Your version of an old master activity and painting by Christine Bleathman and Murray House Mental Health Resource Unit

You could use any famous painting for this activity; in this example, we use Van Gogh's 'Sunflowers'. Each group member will make his or her own sunflower, and then these will be arranged to create the final picture.

You will need several sessions to complete the picture, so run the project over a period of weeks, if possible. If you are in a residential home, leave the picture out, so that night staff can help residents work on it.

## What is needed

- A large piece of cardboard (about 120cm x 90cm) – this could be cut from a box, for example one that contained incontinence pads. Save the rest of the box to make the picture frame and the vase for the sunflowers.
- An old sheet to use as the background to the picture
- Pieces of yellow, orange, brown and green paper, and material for the sunflowers, such as crepe paper, felt and wrapping paper
- Materials for the centre of the sunflowers, such as shredded wheat, bran flakes, chopped walnuts or buttons – use your imagination!
- PVA glue
- Paints and thick felt-tipped pens
- Gold paint

## How it is done

- Make sunflower templates in two different sizes from stiff card. The smaller template is given here.
- Help each person in the group to draw round a template (some people should have larger templates and some smaller ones) and cut out the sunflower. Encourage group members to decorate their sunflower with pieces of paper and material, sticking them down with glue. Draw round the bottom of a glass and cut out the circular piece of card. Glue this to the middle of the decorated sunflower.
- Display the materials for decorating the centre of the sunflower. Encourage group members to use these materials, sticking them with glue to the centre of the sunflower. They could also use a thick brush or sponge to stipple it.
- Staple the sheet to the large piece of cardboard. Cut a picture frame and a vase from cardboard and paint them gold – group

members can help you to do this. Glue these on to the sheet so that the frame covers the staples. Arrange the individual sunflowers on the picture background and glue them on. Finally, paint on stems and glue some real leaves on to complete the picture.

**Try to involve everybody in this group activity. Less able people can help by choosing material for decorating the sunflowers or simply by watching.**

## Variations

Some 'old masters' are particularly suited to collages – for example, Monet's water lilies. To do your own version, tear up blue tissue paper into irregular shapes and glue them onto a piece of card so that it is completely covered. Make the water lilies from white paper serviettes, and the leaves from green card.

# Silk paints on cloth

Silk paints can be used on any natural material such as cotton and polycotton, as well as silk. For those on a budget, old sheets are ideal!

The paints are very attractive vivid colours that mix easily, making successful results easy to achieve. They can be washed out of brushes in water and are fixed by a hot iron, so the process isn't messy or complicated.

You can use the painted material to make cushion covers, tablecloths or wall hangings.

## What is needed

- Silk paints – these are available from art and craft shops, some supermarkets and DIY stores, and catalogues. You need three or four different colours.
- Wood frame to stretch the material on – you can get 27cm square 'batik frames' from craft shops or catalogues. You could make your own by using an old picture frame with the glass removed.
- Drawing pins – the 3-pronged ones from craft shops are best.
- Old sheets or silk, cut a little larger than the size of the frame.
- Paint brushes
- Old jam jars (for water)

### Optional

- Sea salt
- Outliner paint
- Water spray (from a garden shop)

## How it is done

- Wash material if it is new – you could make handwashing it part of the activity. Stretch the washed and dried material over the frame and pin securely.

### Easy method

- Spray the fabric with water or use a large brush to dampen it. This can be a fun and simple activity for a person who is not confident using the paints.
- Encourage people to apply paints to the material in whatever way they choose.
- When enough paint is on the material to make a pattern that covers most of it, leave it to dry.

*Or:*

- Sprinkle sea salt onto the material and then leave it. This creates interesting results as the colours blend and shift, making new patterns as the salt draws the dye towards it.

**More advanced method**

- Draw a pattern or shape onto the material with outliner paint – for example, a flower, a cat, or geometric patterns. Leave the outline to dry.

- Fill in the shapes on dry material. Don't worry if the colours bleed from one shape to another. The effects are usually pleasing anyway.

# Poetry, music and painting

This is a very sensory activity and can stimulate hearing, sight and touch simultaneously. Listening to poetry or music before or during an art activity often inspires people to draw or paint more freely.

## What is needed

- Tubes of quality watercolour paint – poster paints can be used, but the colours are not as rich
- Rolls of wallpaper lining or watercolour paper
- A selection of different sized paintbrushes
- Sponges, cut into strips
- A selection of poetry
- Music and a music system (optional)

## How it is done

- Choose a theme, such as 'autumn', 'Valentine's day', 'children playing' or 'ships at sea'. The theme should relate to either the time of year, or something of interest to people in the group. Choose a poem or piece of writing that is connected to your theme. If you are using music, choose a relevant song or piece of music – for example, a love song for 'Valentine's day' or children's songs and verses for 'children playing'.
- Lay out the roll of paper on a large table, with the brushes and paints ready for use. Seat members of the group around the table.
- Introduce the theme to the group members. Encourage them to think or talk about the first things that come into their mind related to this theme.
- Read out the poem or writing that you have chosen. A member of the group could do this if they wish. You may need to read it a second time, to give people a chance to 'tune in'. Play the music or songs, if you are using them.
- Now invite people to experiment on the paper with colours or patterns related to the theme. The advantage of using one long strip of wallpaper lining is that the group can work on the picture together. This places less emphasis on individual pieces of work, which may be very small.
- At the end of the session, hold up the completed collage and re-read the poem(s) or prose that inspired it.

**People may prefer to talk about the theme or respond to the music instead of painting. This is fine – don't be tempted to rush or over-direct people.**

# Stained glass windows

## What is needed

- Black card or thick paper
- Different coloured tissue paper
- PVA glue
- Scissors
- Glue stick
- Templates
- *Blu-tac*

## How it is done

• Seat everybody around a large table containing all of the equipment needed for the activity.

• Make a template to use as the window using the black card; this is something that you could do beforehand. There are several different designs that you could use, including leaves, a snowman, a fish or a flower. Try to choose seasonally appropriate pictures or pictures that relate to people's interests.

• Cover one side of the black paper template with glue – you could ask for a volunteer from the group to do this. Pass around some sheets of coloured tissue paper and ask the group members to rip them up into smaller pieces. Then stick these to the back of the template, covering all the gaps. Leave to dry. When the template is dry, stick it to a real window with *Blu-tac* so that the light shines through and you can see the beautiful colours that it makes.

**Attaching the tissue paper to the black card template can be fiddly and people might get frustrated and lose interest. However, they might still enjoy other aspects of the activity – for example, choosing a template design or tearing the tissue paper up.**

# Furniture restoration

Old furniture is often available from junk shops for a few pounds. This example is based on restoring an old pine document box. Take care to remove any old nails or splintered wood. This activity is most easily done on a one-to-one basis, as it usually requires a high degree of supervision.

## What is needed:

- Sandpaper – different grades
- Screwdrivers
- Brass cleaning agent
- Wax
- Soft cloth

## How it is done

- Remove the lid and all the metal work, such as handles and hinges. Give the person with dementia some sandpaper and help them to sand down the lid – this is an enjoyable part of the activity because of the quick visible results that it brings. Then turn the box upside down and let the person sand the base as well.
- Give the person the brass bits that you removed from the box. They can polish the brass using a soft cloth and brass cleaner.
- Finally, help the person to apply the wax to the box, buffing with a soft cloth as the work progresses.
- Finally, reassemble the box.

**You must supervise the whole activity.**

**Make sure that all chemicals and tools are stored safely.**

# Reminiscence and life history work

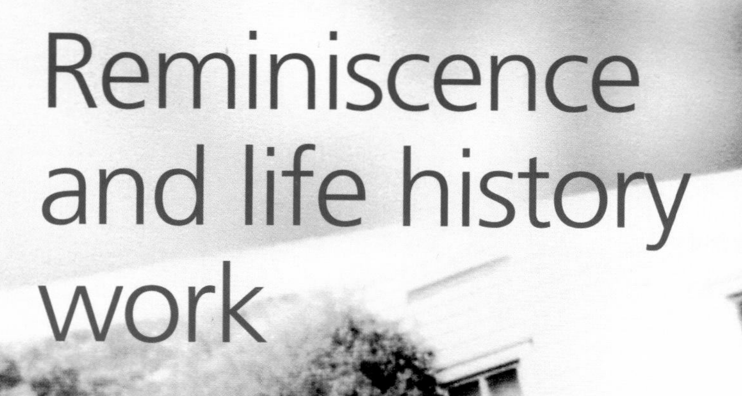

Reminiscence is often used in activities work with older people, usually as a separate session in an activity programme. However, many of the things we do, see or hear remind us of people or situations from our past, and should be considered as reminiscence activities. We should broaden our definition of reminiscence to include these everyday actions.

Reminiscence builds on a person with dementia's strengths, particularly as their long term memories are often better preserved than short term ones. Talking about memories and the people, places and events that matter to a person can be an escape from the difficulties of the present for both the storyteller and the listener.

Photo posed by models

Many people with dementia feel that people are always doing things for them. However, when a person with dementia remembers something and another person is interested in hearing about it, the person becomes a giver again.

Some of the person's recollections might be muddled or hard to follow. They may repeat the same story or confuse the past and the present. An experienced listener can keep 'in tune' with the person despite these difficulties, always making them feel that they matter and that they are being listened to.

Not everybody enjoys reminiscing. Individual assessments are very important in this respect. Reminiscence may involve painful memories; it may also involve memories of happier times that remind a person of their current difficulties. The expression of sadness is not necessarily a bad thing, but care workers must have the skill to respond sensitively.

Sometimes only more confident people in the earlier stages of dementia are involved in reminiscence sessions. This can mean that more reserved people miss opportunities to participate in a meaningful activity. However, be aware that one-to-one time and extra support from staff or volunteers is necessary when including people with advanced levels of dementia in a session.

There are some excellent publications and training courses that give detailed guidance on how to plan structured reminiscence sessions. The Age Exchange Reminiscence Centre in London is a useful resource for people interested in pursuing this work further. Their details are given in 'Helpful organisations' on page 154.

## Considerations

Before beginning any reminiscence sessions, carefully consider the following points.

**DO** **listen carefully** to what a person says and show that you are interested.

**DO** **pay attention to stories that are often repeated** – although it might be boring to hear something for the tenth time, there could be an important message there. Is the person trying to express something about their identity?

**DO** **ask questions and show interest in details** as this gives the person an opportunity to 'dig deeper' into their memory.

**DO** **use props to prompt memories** – objects, pictures, music and dance can all help to 'take people back'.

**DO** **pick up on non-verbal messages** about a person's experience of remembering. Some people will become very animated, while others become more thoughtful or intense.

**DO be aware of diversity** when planning a reminiscence session. If people in your group grew up in countries other than Britain, do some research into what their experiences of childhood and school may have been like. You may need to talk to the person's relatives or make contact with colleagues from a similar cultural background.
– If you are working with younger people with dementia, be aware that appropriate triggers for reminiscing might be very different for a 50-year-old than for a 90-year-old. The Beatles might be a better choice of music than Vera Lynn, for example!
– If you are running a session on memories of courtship, marriage or children, be aware of anyone who has never been married, has been unable to have children or who is a lesbian or gay person. Try widening the topic to memories of love and friendship.
– If you are exploring memories of Christmas, consider whether or not people are from a Christian background, or whether their experience of Christmas is entirely secular.

**DO consider inter-generational opportunities for reminiscence**. Bringing children and older people together to do a piece of work – for example, a play based on the older people's memories – can be very positive for both young and old. You could even do a Christmas pantomime!

**DO be aware of each person's visual and hearing ability**. Acoustics and the arrangement of chairs and tables are very important. A person with a hearing or visual impairment may need someone to sit next to them. If several people are talking at once, it will be hard to follow what is going on; the group leader should be assertive about ensuring that only one person talks at a time.

**DON'T put people on the spot** with specific, direct questions. 'Do you remember…?' can be a very challenging question for a person with memory loss. 'How many children did you have?' might seem like an easy question, but could be very upsetting for a person who cannot remember. Do not allow a reminiscence session to become an interrogation!

**DON'T always correct factual inaccuracies**. Be particularly aware of this when working with relatives and carers; if they know the 'true version' of events, they are often keen for the person to 'get it right'. Sometimes it is important for us to accept an adapted version of a story, as this may be real and important for the person in the present.

**DON'T assume that you have to communicate with words to enjoy reminiscing**. A person with dementia can respond non-verbally to an object or a song that relates to their past. They can also enjoy listening to others' memories and can participate with their eyes and gestures, often as expressive as words.

# A themed reminiscence session

Make sure that you have enough time to plan the session properly and that you have enough members of staff or volunteers to support the group members. Ideally, you need a one-to-one or one-to-two ratio, but with skilled and experienced group workers, a one-to-three ratio may be possible. Each session should have one or two group leaders and some helpers. The group leader(s) hold the structure, while being flexible enough to adapt if unexpected opportunities arise. The helpers attend to people's individual needs; this is often best achieved by pairing helpers with group members.

Plan a mix of different types of activity in each session to hold people's interest and concentration. The example given below is for a two-hour session.

## What is needed

- Props relevant to the theme you have chosen – personal items such as certificates, photographs or clothing can be particularly useful
- Wallpaper lining
- Pencils, paints or felt-tipped pens

## How it is done

Choose a theme. Here are some suggestions:
- Childhood and school days
- Housework and household chores
- Working life
- The local neighbourhood – shops, shopkeepers and other 'local characters'
- Love and friendship
- Days out and holidays
- Nights out and weekends – the cinema, dances, going to church etc
- Buses, trams and automobiles
- Wartime
- Fashion through the ages

If you can identify a common link between a small group of people, you could run a more focused reminiscence group. Here are some ideas:

- Working down the mines.
- Coming to live in Britain from another country. People of similar descent could share experiences or you could work with different cultural groups – for example, African Caribbean and Eastern European – in order to compare experiences. You might need particularly skilled group leaders, especially when working with older refugees who might have traumatic memories.

- Hop-picking holidays in Kent.
- Being 'in service'.

## Example

This example is based on a reminiscence session about working life.

- Firstly, ask everyone to introduce themselves and to say something about their first job. How old were people when they left school and what were their first jobs? Relatives and workers should also share their experiences.

- Divide the group into pairs (one care worker to each group member) and encourage discussions using questions and objects as prompts. These questions should not be asked formally; they should simply assist the helper to start conversations.

- Think of any other ways to raise these subjects – for example, by reading out an extract from a book about someone else's work experience.

Questions you could ask:

**Leaving school and first jobs**
- How did you get your first job?
- What hours did you work?
- Did you have to do any training?
- How did you get to work?
- What do you remember about your boss or your colleagues?

**First wage packets**
- How much were you paid? What did you spend your money on?
- Did you have to give some of it to your family?
- Was it difficult to make ends meet?

**Main job or jobs in life**

- Did you choose your job or was it 'just a job'?
- What was the best thing about the job?
- What was the worst thing?
- What is something you are proud of/an achievement (however small)?
- What advice would you give someone starting out in the job you did?

**Related areas you could ask about**

- Was there a time when you were out of work?
- What work did you do during the war?
- What was it like combining a job and raising a family or running a home?
- Did you ever go on any outings or day trips with your work?

• Now ask the pairs to get into groups of four people. Within each group, ask people to mime jobs that they used to do – for example, driving a van, working in a shop, being a barrister in court or a busy housewife. People could also mime any skills they used in their jobs. You may need to mime an action first and say something like, 'Is this how you did it?' – often, this will encourage the person to correct you! Perform your mimes for other teams and see if they can guess the job.

• Next, do a short drawing exercise. Sit at a table with the group. Place a strip of wallpaper lining and pencils, paints or felt-tipped pens on the table. Invite everybody to draw something related to their work – this could be their uniform, their boss or a piece of equipment etc.

• To finish the session, sit in a big circle and sing some songs related to work – for example, 'Hi ho, hi ho, it's off to work we go!'

# Using a memory box

## What is needed

- A pre-prepared memory box – available from a number of catalogues, including the Alzheimer's Society's

or

- Home-made memory boxes on particular themes, such as 'housework' or 'childhood', or personal boxes for each day centre member or resident

Here are some items that you could include in a memory box:
- Mothballs
- Tin of Brasso
- Hair net
- Sock mushroom
- Fly paper
- Old coins or notes
- Wooden skipping rope
- Nylon stockings
- Stiletto shoes
- A bowler hat
- Old jewellery
- An old-fashioned musical box
- Washing tub and scrubbing brush
- Washing board
- Old pictures
- Old editions of 'Good Housekeeping', 'Picture Post' etc

## How it is done

- Pass one or two items around the group and encourage reactions from each person. They may ask questions, such as, 'What is it?' or comment on it, 'I have one of those at home'. People may take time to examine the object, feel its weight or texture or sniff it.

- Discuss how, why and when these items were used.
- If you are a younger person who is not familiar with the object, ask the group members to tell you about it. If you are familiar with it, draw on your own experience to prompt memories, for example sing a few lines of a skipping rhyme to prompt memories of a skipping rope.

**Be aware of the cultural diversity of your group. You may need to research the different kinds of objects that would evoke memories for people brought up in different countries. Ask for help from relatives or contact a local community organisation from the relevant cultural group. Also carefully consider the age of the people you are working with, especially if they are under 65. Here are some ideas for boxes for people from different cultures.**

Memory boxes for people from different cultures by Jacky Mortimer, 2002

**A memory box for Hong Kong**
Cantonese newspaper
Dried seaweed
Fresh tofu
Picture of a rickshaw
Chinese fabric
Lantern
Chopsticks
Rice noodles
Rice bowl

**A memory box for South Asia**
Indian sweets – gulab jamon, carrot halwa, shrikand (available from the Ambala Sweet Centre, London – tel 020 7387 3521)
Sari fabric
Spices such as cumin, coriander, masala spice mix
Bollywood video
Pictures of Hindi saints

**A memory box for the Caribbean**
Sorrel and ginger tea
Music – soca (calypso), reggae, steel band
A map or pictures of the different islands
Different types of food, such as sugar cane, plantain, okra, coconut, yam and watermelon
Bandana
Bright clothes
Carnival pictures showing costumes
Cricket bat
Beach shells
Pictures of tropical fish
Hibiscus flower

# 'This is your life' – making a personal journal or photograph album

This activity is best shared between a person with dementia, their key worker and a relative. You will need to look through old photographs and record the person's memories, which could take a number of sessions over a period of weeks, and be very involved.

People often enjoy the attention and interest in their life that this activity entails. A carer might like to be reminded of their relative's strengths and of happier times, and may also learn new things about the person. A key worker will have an opportunity to learn more about the relationships, events and experiences that shaped that person's life.

The book produced by this activity may be a helpful resource for the staff team working with the person. It may also be extremely helpful if the person has to move into another care setting.

## What is needed

- A selection of photographs and other memorabilia from the person's past
- A scrap book or photograph album in which to compile the person's memories

## How it is done

- You could divide the book up into the stages of a person's life:
  - *childhood*: birthplace, home life, parents/grandparents, siblings, early education, pets
  - *adolescence*: school, favourite subjects, friends, interests, hobbies, sports
  - *young adulthood:* further education, jobs, marriage/relationships, family, clubs, first home, military service
  - *middle age*: grandchildren, hobbies, work, travel, family role, clubs
  - *later years*: life achievements, hobbies, travel, family

- Alternatively, you could divide the book up into themes such as 'important people', 'special places', 'memorable events', 'hobbies and interests', 'favourite foods' and so on.

- You could focus on key areas relating to the person's identity. For example, someone's experience of working on a ship, raising a large family or travelling all over the world.

- If you are short of photographs, think creatively about using other pictures that could remind someone of a part of their life. Any picture of men in navy uniform for an ex-service man or of children playing on a beach for memories of seaside holidays might work just as well.

- Celebrate the finished work with an event. You could do an imitation of the 'This is Your Life' programme and invite a few people who are important to the person to come to the home or day centre to hear extracts from the book.

**Be aware of the emotions that an exploration of a person's life might provoke. Photographs of a person's mother or father, for example, might evoke feelings of sadness and loss. Reminiscence work should only be done by a care worker with the skill and sensitivity to respond understandingly to these emotions.**

**Some people with dementia will struggle to recognise faces and remember names of people in photographs. Watch out for signs that a person is becoming frustrated.**

# Compiling a family tree

A person with dementia is more likely to remember people from the past, such as siblings and parents, than they are more recent additions to the family. However, people can get much pride and satisfaction from seeing how their family has grown and is continuing to evolve. A family tree is a good way to track these changes.

## What is needed

- A large sheet of paper
- Coloured pens and pencils
- Photographs of the person's family members (optional)

## How it is done

Draw a family tree with the help of the person with dementia and, possibly, their carer. You could draw a traditional family tree with lines and names or you could use colours and pictures to bring the tree to life. For example, you could draw a picture of a cake for someone's mother if they did a lot of baking, use different colours for boys and girls, or use photographs of some of the most important family members.

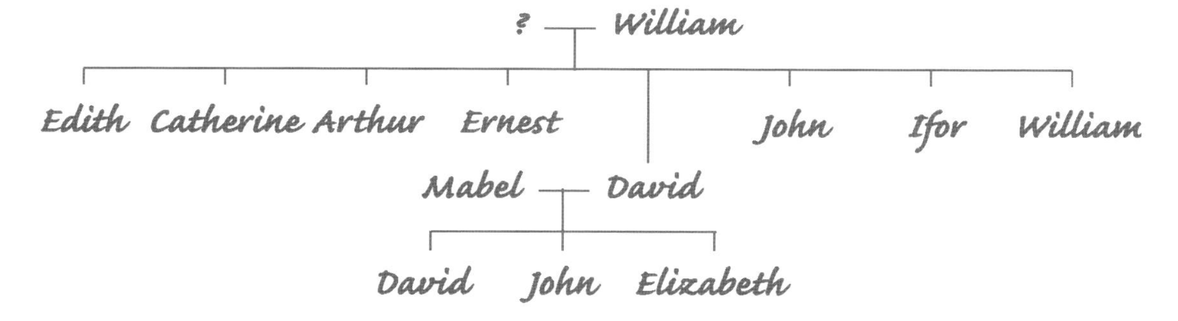


## Life history questionnaire

Pre-prepared questions can be useful when working on family trees with an individual or a small group of people. If you go through these questions in a group, people can enjoy chatting about their answers. Please see Appendix 2 *Life history notes* for a list of suggested questions.

Avoid using these questions too formally, as you could make the person feel pressured. Only ask more personal questions when the person feels sufficiently comfortable and safe with you.

## Likes and dislikes

You could also fill in the likes and dislikes inventory in Appendix 2 to get an idea of a person's life history.

# Life experiences snap

## What is needed

- Sheets of paper
- Pens

## How it is done

- On each sheet of paper, draw six or eight boxes, like on a bingo card.
- Choose a category – for example, 'Jobs I have done in my life', 'Family life' or 'Things that I am proud of'.
- Talk to each person about the things that are relevant to them in the category you have chosen and write one example in each box. For example, if the category is jobs, write a different job that the person has done in each box.

| | | |
|---|---|---|
| Junior office clerk | cleaner | WRAF (in war) |
| housewife/mother | nursery school helper | shopkeeper |

- Bring together a small group of people who have all created their own card. Invite one person in the group to call out one of their jobs. If another person has done the same job, they shout 'Snap!' The care worker running the activity then encourages the pair to compare notes about that job.
- Both people then cross out that job from their card and another person calls out another job. If they are the only person to have done that job, they call out another example from their card.
- There is no 'winner' in this game – people can get satisfaction from knowing they are the only person in the group to have done a job or from feeling that they share a similar experience with other group members.
- Staff members should also make cards, as this can provide an interesting point of connection between staff and clients.

# Memories of local area

This is a good activity for a group of people who have lived in an area for a long time, and may have similar memories of places or events there.

## What is needed

- Old cine films of the area or a video of local streets and key landmarks such as churches and shops
- Photographs or old newspaper extracts from the local area
- Local history books
- Paper and pencils

## How it is done

- Ask someone from the local history section of your library to help you collect books, photographs and information about the area. Perhaps they could also give an informal talk at your centre or home. Otherwise, do some research of your own about the area, particularly about the period when the people you are working with were younger.
- Show people in your group pictures or films to help prompt memories.
- Talk about incidents that occurred in the area, shops or markets that people used regularly, clubs or associations that they may have belonged to, and places they may have visited for a fun night out or at weekends.
- You could, as a group, draw the main highstreet or shopping centre as it used to be in the past, adding any names of shops or shopkeepers that people might remember.
- Make a trip into town with members of the group to look at some familiar local landmarks – be aware that some places may not be easily recognisable. Some museums may have local history sections, with pictures and displays that could prompt memories.

**The most well-known events in a place's history are often tragedies such as railway disasters, bombs or murders, as these are highlighted by the press. Always find out whether any individuals in your group had personal associations with such events.**

**Places may provoke memories of relatives or friends who have now died. Be prepared to respond to sad memories or more complex emotions.**

### Variations

If you are working with a group of people who come from different parts of the country or the world, explore this diversity as a point of interest and discussion. Put a map of the UK or the world on the wall, and talk about where individuals were born and where they lived. Compare memories of the weather, school days, shops, celebrations or national recipes.

EXAMPLE

### Local memories

Following consultation of local maps, one care worker visited a number of cemeteries and churchyards in the Carlisle area with one of his clients. The client was very interested in old gravestones and in reading about family histories. On one occasion, both the client and the worker were fascinated to learn about a famous rail incident that occurred in the 1920s.

## 'Treasured memories' board game

This game is available from Winslow Press – see 'Useful publications and resources' on page 157.

It consists of a game board, question cards and action cards, coloured markers and dice. It can be played with two to eight players.

The advantage of the game is that it offers a structured opportunity for prompting reminiscence combined with the social interaction and pleasure of participating in a board game.

Individuals can be involved at various levels, including throwing the dice, moving the markers, reading out a question, performing a particular action for others to guess or discussing the questions about the past.

# Gardening

Many people develop an interest in gardening in later life. The contact with nature, the pleasure of watching things grow, the enjoyment of gentle physical activity and the sensory pleasures of the garden seem to engage people more as they age and contemplate their own position in the cycle of life. The combination of practical and psychological or spiritual qualities makes gardening an enriching activity for those experiencing loss and stress.

Adapted with permission from 'Using outdoor spaces for people with dementia – a carer's perspective', Martin Cobley, *Working with older people*, June 2002, Vol 6, issue 2

Gardens offer many sensory-rich experiences involving sight, touch, smell, taste and hearing. There are the colours and shapes of flowers and foliage and the play of light and shadow on trees and lawns. There are different textures – from smooth, velvety leaves, to the roughness of bark. There are light breezes and the smells of flowers, herbs and freshly mown grass. We can taste freshly picked raspberries, tomatoes and mint, and hear leaves rustling, insects buzzing and birds singing.

Gardening can help people to express themselves and can reinforce their sense of self. Outdoor activities – or indoor activities using seasonal items – can also remind a confused person of the time of day and time of year. Sharing a gardening experience can help reinforce intimacy. A private corner of the garden may provide space to acknowledge grief and other emotions, or to talk about difficult issues. People can plant a tree, shrub or bulbs in remembrance of somebody or to help them cope with bereavement. Observing the life and death cycles of nature may also be a way of sharing spiritual beliefs; people can take produce to church as part of the harvest thanksgiving, for example.

Caring for plants may relieve feelings of helplessness and dependency. Short term memory loss might mean that people don't always recognise the daily and weekly continuity in gardening tasks, and the enjoyment of watching things grow may be reduced. However, gardening activities offer plenty of 'here and now' sensory experiences that people with dementia can respond to.

There are many different ways of engaging people with dementia in gardening activities. These include:

- involving people in the design, care and upkeep of the day centre or care home garden
- helping people to tend to window-sill pots and indoor plants in their own room
- acquiring an allotment, conservatory or greenhouse in order to grow flowers and/or vegetables
- starting a 'gardening club' so that a group of people can work on gardening projects together on a regular basis.

Gardening provides opportunities for people at all stages of dementia. A person can be involved through potting, watering and tending for plants sitting in a wheelchair in a living room, or through digging and pushing a wheelbarrow outside.

Adapted with permission from a diagram by S Gaspar, NAPA

# Designing a garden for people with dementia

Plan the garden carefully before doing any work on it. It must accommodate the physical, psychological and cultural needs of the people who will be using it, and these people should be consulted as far as possible in the early stages. It is relatively easy to adapt gardens over time as needs become clearer or change – therefore, you don't have to get it completely right first time. Here are some of the most important things to consider:

- Gardens should be accessible for people who use wheelchairs.
- Provide protection from both bright sunlight and chilling winds; avoid deep shade.
- Solid boundaries will make the garden feel safe and enclosed.
- You may need to screen areas surrounding the garden and disguise gates to discourage people from 'wandering'.
- People in the garden should be visible from adjacent windows if they are using the garden unaccompanied.
- Paths should have a straightforward layout – sometimes a loop is best so that it takes the visitor on a journey.
- Trees and features like sculptures can act as landmarks to help with navigation.
- Create sitting areas with focal points to look at, such as a display of bedding plants, a bird table or a small statue.
- Design the garden to stimulate the senses – use colourful, fragrant plants and flowers, water features and wind chimes.
- Use plants that will attract birds and beneficial insects such as ladybirds, bees, butterflies and grasshoppers.
- Use gentle changes rather than sharp contrasts in paving materials, colour, light and shade. Avoid:
  - shadows on paths, which might look like holes
  - abrupt changes of paving materials and levels
  - reflective materials, which might look like water.
- Prompt reminiscence by incorporating plants and garden features familiar to the users of the garden, where possible. Local plants and features might help reinforce an understanding of the current place and environment.
- Avoid hazards such as slippery fallen leaves or berries in autumn, ice in winter and overhanging branches.
- Avoid plants, trees and shrubs which may cause injury when touched or grasped (stinging nettles are an obvious example; and anything with thorns, spikes or spines is best avoided).
- Similarly, avoid anything which could be harmful if ingested. Part or all of a plant may be poisonous or cause irritation or choking (an example of the latter is the fine hairs inside rosehips).

**Be aware of plants that are poisonous or whose sap is an irritant affecting skin, eyes or stomach if ingested, particularly if anyone you are working with is inclined to put things in their mouths. Some of the more common poisonous plants are convalaria (lily of the valley), hellebore (winter or lenten rose), ivy, yew and woody nightshade. Check the label if there is one or ask at your local florist or garden centre. A good reference book might help as a last resort, and if all else fails, err on the side of caution and don't use the plant!**

## Emergency aid

**In the event of a suspected poisoning:**

- DO NOT attempt to make the individual sick; this may be harmful.
- Even if no symptoms are present, ensure the individual IMMEDIATELY visits a GP or hospital's accident and emergency department. Take a sample of the plant with you.
- Record the time of eating and note any symptoms. These may occur many hours later.

**For skin or eye irritation:**

- Wash the skin area or eye affected with clean water and protect from sunlight.
- If in doubt or if symptoms persist, seek medical advice as above as soon as possible.
- Remember to take a sample of the plant(s) with you for identification.

## Conventional gardening activities

These are some of the basic conventional garden activities:

**Planning** – This can provide continuity during the winter when the scope for other gardening tasks is limited. It can involve reading seed and plant catalogues and gardening magazines; watching gardening programmes; walking around the home or day centre's garden; visiting local garden centres, perhaps taking photographs; having discussions and drawing plans.

**Preparing the ground/hard landscaping** – Digging and turning the soil or lifting stones to build a rockery can be satisfying work for physically fit and strong people. Those who cannot manage the physical labour may enjoy watching and offering their expertise!

**Sowing seed and taking cuttings** – This can be done indoors or outside. Indoors is easier for people with limited mobility; these activities are also possible for people in bed. You will need some space indoors or in a sheltered place outdoors (such as a cold frame) and someone who will take responsibility for ensuring that watering and

nurture are adequate. Plants started off indoors which are ultimately to be planted outdoors need to be 'hardened off' (gradually acclimatised over a week or two to weather conditions by being put outside for increasing periods of time).
Working with small items such as seed, seedlings and cuttings helps promote co-ordination and dexterity.

**Potting up and planting out** – Small plants and bulbs can be planted in containers to go indoors or out as well as in beds outdoors. This provides physical exercise and creativity in the choice and arrangement of plants. To get all year round value, put outdoor containers near windows where they can be seen from inside.

**Maintenance tasks** – Weeding or hoeing, watering, deadheading (ie removing dead flower heads to encourage the production of fresh blooms), pruning and clipping are all necessary to keep the garden looking its best. If this is too much work, you can pay a maintenance contractor to do it for you.

## Tools and protective clothing

Many gardening activities can be done sitting at benches or tables. Raised beds and containers will help wheelchair users take part in other activities too. Make sure there are also tools available to accommodate other physical disabilities. You will need hand tools such as trowels, forks and dibbers (for making holes in compost for large seeds or cuttings) as well as larger tools like spades, forks, rakes, hoes, watering cans and hosepipes. Place tools just out of reach – this means that people have to stretch and bend a little more, thereby increasing the intensity of the exercise. Extra supervision will be needed if people are using sharp tools such as shears and secateurs or electrical equipment such as strimmers or hedge trimmers; these should be fitted with circuit breakers in case the electrical cable is accidentally severed.

Older people may have difficulty kneeling down. Knee pads and knee rests with low rails at the sides to help the person stand up are available to buy, but you can improvise with old cushions, chair seats or pieces of foam rubber in a plastic sleeve. Specialist tools cater for other physical limitations; information on these is available from the Disabled Living Foundation (see 'Helpful organisations' on page 154).

Also consider protective clothing such as gloves and aprons. This may be a personal preference rather than a necessity – people might want to wear gloves if they don't like handling 'dirty' soil or compost. Wearing thinner gloves will enable a person to carry out 'fiddly' tasks more easily. People should wear old clothes when working in the garden. Clothing to protect against the weather might also be necessary – for example, sun hats, warm pullovers or coats.

## Seasonal gardening tasks

There are tasks for every season in a garden, not just summer days; a greenhouse or conservatory will provide opportunities for activities when the weather gets cold or wet. If your space outside is limited, use window boxes, hanging baskets and planters on patios, or garden indoors with pot plants and house plants.

**Spring**

- Sow seeds in pots and trays and plant summer bulbs in pots.
- Re-pot small plants into larger containers or plant them out in the ground.
- Prune shrubs and clip hedges.
- Visit a farm to order manure for mulching.
- Dig over vegetable patches, adding manure.
- Sow seeds in the vegetable patch or flower borders.

**Summer**

- Water plants with a watering can or a hose.
- Use a push mower to cut the grass.
- Weed flower borders and the vegetable patch.
- Do 'dead heading'.
- Take cuttings.

**Autumn**

- Plant spring bulbs.
- Wash flower pots.
- Sweep leaves.
- Build a compost heap.
- Make a bonfire.

**Winter**

- Clean and oil garden tools, maintain garden furniture.
- Paint or creosote a fence, seat, or bird table.
- Look at seed, bulb and plant catalogues.
- Plan the garden for the following year.

**All year round:**

- Examine the garden and enjoy the beauty of its plants and flowers.
- Put kitchen waste on the compost heap.

- Observe the weather conditions and the contrast between indoors and outdoors, for example in coming in from the cold to a hot cup of tea on a winter's day.
- Visit a garden centre or a garden that is open to the public (including the tea room!) to buy plants or just to look at them.

## Some tips for successful gardening

- Horticultural terms ('dead heading', 'hardening off' etc) and the Latin names used for plants along with their common names can be confusing for a person new to gardening. Get a good 'gardening for beginners' book from your library or bookshop – you will soon start to pick up knowledge.
- Think about what will grow best in the type of soil in your locality – look at the plants, shrubs and trees growing successfully nearby. Also think about where in your garden plants will grow best. Observe which parts of the garden are sunny or shady at different times of the day and which parts have dry or boggy ground during the year.
- Virtually all plants growing in the ground will benefit from having a 5-10cm layer of compost spread around them in early spring (a 'mulch'). This replaces the nutrients that have been used up by the plants the previous year or that have been washed out of the soil by winter rain. The term 'compost' might be confusing to the novice. It refers to nutritious matter created by organic material rotting down over a number of months. Compost can be bought – different grades are available depending on what it's to be used for. Be kind to our boglands and avoid commercial composts that include peat. Compost can be made easily in a heap in a shady, hidden corner of the garden. Alternatives to compost are well-rotted manure or chemical fertilisers.

## Gardening without a garden

Gardening is possible without a garden – use containers on a patio or hanging baskets instead. Some tips for growing plants in containers:

- Ensure they have good drainage by putting a layer of gravel or broken terracotta flower pots ('crocks') in the bottom to cover the container's drainage hole(s).
- Ensure the plants are watered regularly. Help water soak in by not overfilling the container with compost. To help water reach the roots of plants in deep containers, insert a short pipe vertically into the soil at the time of planting and pour water down it.
- If the containers are permanent, ensure the plants are fed regularly, either by regular liquid feeds during the growing season and/or a yearly mulch.

## Activities using things from the garden

There is a wealth of activities that can be done indoors using plant material, from examining and talking about items to doing crafts using them. Although the quickest, cheapest, most convenient and most satisfying way of getting plant material is to grow plants yourself, you can get them from a supermarket, florist or garden centre instead. Alternatively, ask relatives and friends to bring things in from their own gardens (check that plants aren't potentially harmful, as mentioned on pages 106 and 107). Don't pick things from the countryside – look after our wildlife! If you are picking things from private property (such as a park or a field), get permission from the owner.

Here are some ideas for using things from the garden:

- Arrange flowers, leaves and twigs, living or dried, perhaps supplemented by artificial items such as ribbon bows secured to the end of a stout wire or cane.
- Press flowers to make pictures, greetings cards or book marks.
- Use leaves and potato prints in art sessions to make pictures or greetings cards, or to press into clay to make patterns.
- Dry lavender or other fragrant flowers and herbs to make lavender bags, moth bags (use thyme, mint, rosemary, sage, sweet marjoram or lavender), herb pillows or pot pourri.
- Use herbs in a bath. Make small cotton or muslin drawstring bags to put herbs in, or use the bags leftover from laundry detergent tablets available from supermarkets and hang the bags over the bath taps as the water is running.
- Prepare and eat produce from the garden. You can use home-grown herbs in cooking, prepare home-grown runner beans, shell peas and broad beans and prepare fruit for a fruit salad.

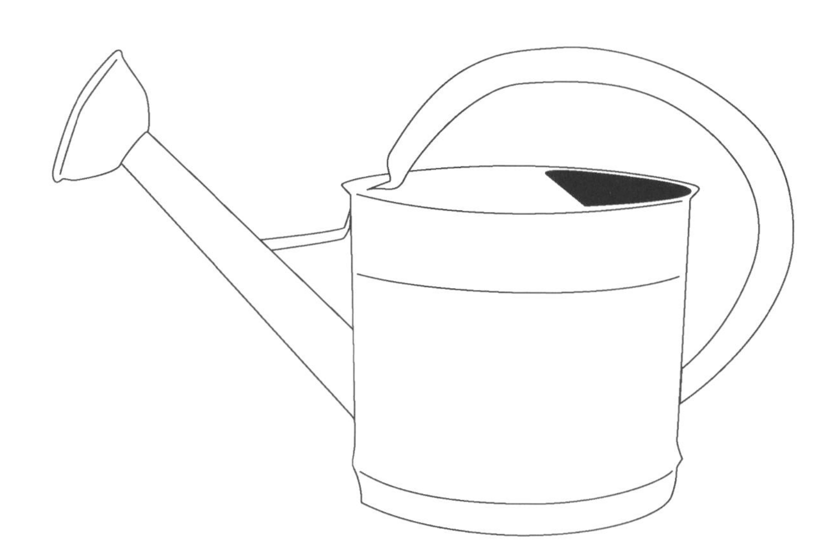

# Examining plants, flowers, fruit and vegetables

Simply looking at and talking about garden produce can be an enjoyable activity. Bringing items indoors may be the easiest way of doing this; alternatively, move into the garden and look at them in situ, or organise a trip to a local garden or garden centre.

## What is needed:

- A selection of flowers, leaves, fruit, vegetables, weeds and herbs – use anything you can find! (As explained on pages 106 and 107, though, beware of anything that might be harmful – always check first.)
- Photographs of plants and gardens (optional)

## How it is done:

• If you are doing this activity indoors, seat everybody around a table with all of the material you are going to look at in the centre. You could start the session with a competition to name all of the items – this usually gets people in the mood!

• Give people plenty of time to examine the various items; don't over-direct the group. People may spontaneously talk about their associations with things and the memories they evoke. You could ask people which flowers or plants they like best and why, or point out the variety of colours and scents.

• Here are some ideas for conversations that you could have about the plants and flowers. Allow everyone to contribute and change the direction of the conversation as they like.

  - How garden produce was used during the Second World War – for example, Digging for Victory. People also had to use unusual ingredients and recipes because of rationing, eating things like beetroot cake, scrambled onions, sugar beet soup and primrose tart. Some people collected rose hips and other wild plants for the authorities to use in foodstuffs and drugs. People may remember rosebay willow herb which grew on bombsites during and after the war.
  - Childhood memories of making daisy chains, playing 'he loves me, he loves me not', making a wish whilst blowing a dandelion 'clock' seed head, playing conkers and picking blackberries.
  - The names, history and folklore of indigenous plants and garden 'weeds'. Ask people what they know about them and what names they used for them. Local names for plants vary around the country. For example, primula veris (cowslip) has many

names: 'St Peter's keys', 'key flower', 'herb Peter', 'Our Lady's bunch of keys', 'Our Lady's cushion', 'galligaskins' and 'jackanapes on horses'.

- Remedies made from plants, for example rubbing dock leaves on nettle stings to soothe them and eating raw onions to help stop colds.
- Folklore and old sayings, such as, 'When gorse is in blossom, kissing's in season'. It was said that a child picking dandelions would wet the bed and that wild hawthorn warded off evil – although bringing cut branches indoors invited death.

# Taking geranium cuttings

Taking cuttings is the quickest way of getting new plants. The results are more immediate than planting seeds and waiting for them to grow. Geraniums (more correctly called pelargoniums by plant purists!) are easy to propagate in this way and it can be done at any time of year.

Geraniums will grow indoors or out, although they need protection from frost. This is best achieved by planting them in pots, which can be brought indoors to a sunny window-sill or into a greenhouse during winter.

There are several types of geranium: the bedding and trailing varieties have brightly-coloured, long-lasting flower spikes, and the scented-leaved varieties have dainty and old-fashioned looking flowers. Scented-leaved geraniums come in a variety of 'scents', such as lemon and sandalwood. When brushed, a large pot of these in your garden will give off the scent; or pick a small leaf and rub it between your fingers.

## What is needed

- Flower pots
- Moist seed or potting compost (spray it with water if it's too dry)
- A blade or knife
- A cutting surface, for example an old kitchen chopping board
- Geranium mother plants
- A dibber (you can use an old pencil or pen)
- Thin gloves (optional if people don't like handling the compost)

## How it is done

- Fill a medium-sized flower pot with at least 5cm of potting compost and press it down.
- You can pot cuttings individually or put several in a large pot. Use the dibber to make a hole in the compost about 5cm deep.
- Cut a 10cm-long green shoot that hasn't yet produced flowers from the mother plant (pinch out any small flower buds that you can see). Gently pull away all except the top three leaves and carefully trim the cutting with a sharp blade or knife 2-3mm below a leaf join.
- Put the cutting in the hole and press the compost firmly around it.
- Water sparingly, by placing the pot in 2cm of water for half an hour.
- Put the pot in a bright, warm place indoors but out of direct sunlight.
- Spray the cuttings daily with a fine mister. Alternatively, put a polythene bag or a clear plastic bottle (with its bottom cut off and screw top removed) over the pot. This will help to maintain a humid microclimate. Remove the bag or bottle for half an hour each day to allow air to circulate, thus reducing the risk of the cuttings going rotten.
- The cuttings should root within a few weeks.

## Variations

Geranium cuttings will also root fairly easily in water as long as the stems haven't become too woody. It is fun to watch the roots develop and a glass container will allow them to be seen more easily (although better roots will develop if a solid or brown glass container is used). Eventually the rooted cuttings can be potted up. A piece of charcoal (available from pet shops or garden centres offering aquarium supplies) will help keep the water healthy.

You could fill the container with clean pebbles or marbles, so that the cuttings can stand up. The display will last longer if you feed the cuttings regularly with very diluted liquid feed such as Baby Bio. Traditional house plants can be grown particularly well in this way: try tradescantia (wandering jew), philodendron (sweetheart plant), chlorophytum (spider plant), plectranthus (Swedish ivy), rhoicissus (grape ivy) and coleus, for example.

Alternatively, put the tops of vegetables such as carrots, parsnips and turnips in a flatter bowl with water. The vegetable top should be about 2cm thick. Watch the ferny leaves grow as well as the roots. The vegetable slices won't grow any bigger, so this is purely decorative!

# Making a miniature indoor garden

Making a miniature indoor garden offers great scope for creativity and can be done at any time of year – it is particularly good to do during winter, when there are less other gardening activities to do. This example uses air plants, supplemented with dried flowers or grasses and some artificial items. Air plants don't need compost and are easy to maintain indoors. They can go for a couple of weeks without watering and are difficult to over-water. To water the plants, either remove them and submerge them in water for an hour or two every week or spray them frequently with water using a fine mister.

## What is needed

- An old plastic lid, small tray or bowl for the base
- Several species of air plants (available from garden centres and florists)
- Gravel, small stones and pebbles
- Small pieces of driftwood, shells, animal ornaments and artificial flowers to use as decoration
- Glue or wire (and pliers to cut it) to fix decorative items in place
- Gloves, if plants or other items are spiky
- Fine water spray cannister (available from garden centres)

## How it is done

- Help the person making the arrangement to plan their garden. You will need to think about which things need to be glued down and which will stay put under their own weight.
- Glue down the dried flowers and other decorative items, and arrange the stones and pebbles so that they cover any gaps. Firmly lodge the air plants in suitable holes, perhaps in nooks or crannies between rocks or branches.
- Discuss the final effect with the person or people who made the garden. Are they happy with it? What would they change? Make sure that the garden is put somewhere highly visible and encourage people to talk about it and spray it with water when necessary.

## Variations

- Using compost in your miniature garden will give a wider range of plants to choose from than just air plants. However, the dry, centrally heated indoor environment in homes and day centres can be detrimental to some plants, so choose them carefully. Overcome the problem of watering regularly by using succulents, which can tolerate dry conditions. If the container does not have holes in the bottom, put a layer of pebbles or charcoal at the bottom for drainage. Fill the container with seed compost, potting compost mixed with sand or special succulent compost and plant the plants. Avoid spiky or spiny plants such as cacti, agave or aloe; use instead any of the following: bryophyllum (good luck plant), crassula argentea (jade plant), echeveria, sedum, sempervivum (houseleek), senecio (string of beads plant) or kalanchoë. Place the garden in a sunny position such as a south-facing window-sill; water sparingly, especially in winter.

• If the environment is hot and dry from central heating, and other house plants don't survive well, consider using a terrarium or plant case – these are sealed so that a humid microclimate exists inside them. You can use a fishtank with a clear perspex or clingfilm top (slope the roof so that condensation doesn't drop on the plants but trickles down the walls), sweet jars on their side, carbuoys or other large bottles.

• Choose slow growing plants. Don't use succulents as the atmosphere will be too moist and they will rot, and don't use flowering plants unless you can snip off the dead flower heads. Suitable foliage plants are ferns, fittonia (snakeskin plant), ficus pumila (creeping fig), peperomia, pilea (aluminium plant) and saxifraga sarmentosa (mother of thousands).

• Before you begin, wash the container in warm water and washing up liquid. Put charcoal pieces in the bottom and add potting compost mixed with coarse sand. Use a dryish mixture so it doesn't stick to the sides of the container; a piece of cardboard rolled into a funnel will help fill small-necked containers such as bottles. You might need to use long-handled tools such as plastic forks or spoons taped to the end of short canes to plant up bottles. To press down the compost, use a cane with a cotton reel pushed firmly on the end. These jobs are fiddly and people with poor eye-sight or co-ordination may struggle. However, they can choose the plants and plan the garden – and they may find it entertaining to watch you try to create the garden! Decorate the soil using washed stones or pebbles, and add clean gravel using a spoon on a stick.

• Place the terrarium in a bright position but out of direct sunlight. For the first week, watch for misting and if it occurs, remove the seal or lid until it has cleared and seal it up again. Regular watering shouldn't be necessary because the water inside is recycled, but occasionally a top-up might be needed. Once the plants are established and you need to keep them small, tape a scalpel blade to the end of a cane to use as a cutting tool and spear to pick up the prunings.

# Food, fun and parties

Food offers many opportunities for fun, creativity and excitement. Preparing food stimulates our senses and provides a sense of purpose and expectation. Sharing a meal is also a great social opportunity. Mealtimes in institutional settings often take up a large part of the day. It is important to make the most of these opportunities for stimulation, interaction and pleasure.

Many people feel that they are not very good at cooking. For this reason, you may come across initial resistance to doing 'cooking' as part of an activity. This applies both to people with dementia and care workers! It is sometimes a good idea to follow a new recipe with your group, so that you are all 'in the same boat', following unfamiliar instructions. People in the group are then more likely to contribute instead of simply following your lead.

Sometimes, care workers are reluctant to do cooking activities with people who have dementia because they fear that there are too many potential risks involved. These risks involve food safety and hygiene as well as the use of knives, hot ovens and other potentially dangerous equipment. However, with good assessment and planning many of these risks can easily be anticipated and minimised.

There is not room in this book to provide many specific recipes, and there are countless good cookery books on the market. For these reasons, we have provided a few examples, which illustrate how you can involve people with dementia in cooking. You can build on and adapt these recipes if you wish. You can focus on food that is familiar to people, particularly if you want to prompt conversation and reminiscence. However, if you are working with people from different cultural backgrounds, it might be enjoyable for them to show other people in the group how to prepare some of their own traditional meals.

In an ideal world, it would be best to involve people with dementia in the preparation of everyday meals on a regular basis, rather than only organising specific 'cooking activities'.

## General tips for a cooking activity

- Allow enough time to buy the ingredients and collect the equipment you need. Think about taking clients with you to do this.
- Nominate one member of staff to stay at the same place at the table during the activity. This helps to establish a group spirit and a sense of security, even when other members of staff have to move about to attend to other people.
- Don't be too ambitious – keep it simple.
- Remember that people can be involved in tasks of varying complexity. These include sitting and watching, handling the ingredients, reading a recipe, weighing, counting, measuring, pouring, stirring, passing things, mixing, rolling, cutting, decorating and tasting. Make sure you involve everybody.
- Avoid high-risk activities, such as deep-frying chips, for example. Preparing cold food can be satisfying and less stressful. It also enables people to taste the food as they work – one of the pleasures of cooking!

EXAMPLE

## Everyday food preparation

Some expert colleagues in the dementia care field recently observed the Sunnydale Day Centre throughout one day. The feedback was positive, but suggested that more could be made of lunchtime at the centre. Lunchtime was seen as a routine event to be got through quite quickly and was often over within 40 minutes. This resulted in long afternoons, with many day centre members getting impatient to go home.

The staff team decided to rethink lunch as one of the main activities of the day. They considered all of the different jobs involved in preparing, serving and clearing up after the meal. They met with kitchen staff to talk about any aspects of food preparation that could be done by day centre members. They also negotiated with managers about health and safety issues, including food hygiene. This resulted in some day centre members doing food preparation, such as peeling potatoes and carrots, shelling peas and making desserts.

Individual menu cards were redesigned in a clear and bright way and staff and members used them as a discussion point in the run-up to lunch. Some people helped lay the tables, prepared fresh flowers for the vases and poured drinks, others folded the serviettes, and the most able clients helped serve the food. A talkative and leisurely atmosphere was encouraged during the meal itself. The choice of drinks served at lunch (previously just orange or blackcurrant) was widened. After lunch, time was set aside for clearing the dishes. Whilst some people washed and dried up, others enjoyed a cup of tea or coffee and a chocolate.

The lunchtime period now lasted nearly two hours and was the focal point of the day! Staff members reported that although they had to work hard, they now really enjoyed mealtimes and felt that they had created a 'sense of community' amongst clients and staff.

- Ensure that there are enough utensils to allow each group member to do something. Avoid using industrial size utensils from the main kitchen, as they are less familiar and domestic looking.
- Try to use traditional utensils that your clients may be familiar with – for example, earthenware mixing bowls, enamel pie plates and preserving jars. You could also include kitchen equipment used by different ethnic groups, such as stainless steel pans, woks, chopsticks and bamboo steamers, to help people from different backgrounds feel comfortable and involved.
- Make sure you have enough staff to allow one staff member to work with a group of no more than two or three people with dementia.

- Think about how to engage quieter people. Bear in mind any sight or hearing impairments when organising seating arrangements.
- Have some wet wipes or warm flannels near by for sticky fingers and faces!
- Use lots of conversation, and create a sense of friendship and intimacy by encouraging reminiscence, laughter and song.

## Food related social events

Food and eating can be incorporated into many social events. These can be fun and provide good opportunities for people with dementia to mix with each other, friends and family, and other people in the community. Here are some ideas:

- A 'fish and chips' quiz night
- A barbecue
- A coffee morning with guests from outside the day centre or care home – you could also have a raffle or bring-and-buy sale
- A garden tea party
- An evening drinks party

- A formal dinner to celebrate an anniversary or birthday – people can dress up and staff and or clients/residents can act as waiters and waitresses
- A picnic in a park or gardens
- A slap-up breakfast in bed, served in style!
- A romantic meal for two in a restaurant

- A Wimbledon tennis party with strawberries and champagne or an Ascot event with special hats

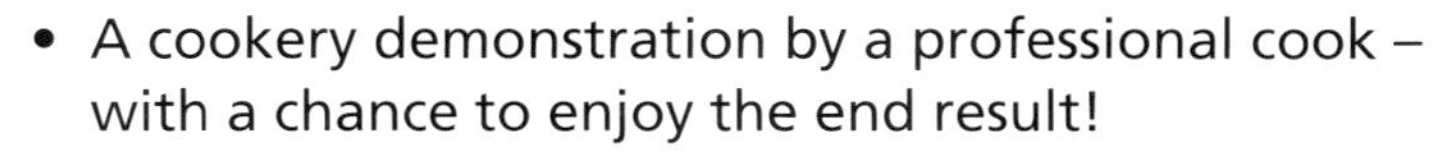

- A cookery demonstration by a professional cook – with a chance to enjoy the end result!

- A themed event, for example a Hawaiian tropical day, a Chinese night, a Valentine's day meal or a midsummer's day garden party
- A celebration of religious festivals with appropriate food – for example, doughnuts at Chanukah in the Jewish religion or hot cross buns at Easter in the Christian tradition.

## Treats for every day

Food is an everyday pleasure and therefore should be integrated into everyday life in a care setting. If someone enjoys chocolates, sweets or alcohol or has a particular preference such as dried fruit with their cereal or hot milk before bed, ensure that their care plan includes these simple pleasures.

EXAMPLE

### A Hawaiian tropical day

Prepare a good selection of appropriate music and sounds, including steel band music and perhaps the sound of waves crashing on a beach.

Select some nice smelling lotions, such as banana, coconut or lemon, for hand and feet massages. Fizzy bath bombs with floral and fruit smells can be put in tubs of warm water to soak people's feet.

Prepare some fresh fruit punches with various fruit juices and sparkling wine or rum for the adventurous! Set out some bowls of tropical fruit.

In the build up to the day, involve people in making garlands to wear round their necks and pictures of parrots, palm trees and so on to put on the walls. Put some tropical flowers around the room.

Encourage staff and clients to wear beach and party clothes in bright colours and Hawaiian prints.

As one care worker said, 'Life is about new ideas and experiences. When staff say that they don't understand and it won't work, don't worry – one successful Hawaiian day will have them all limbo dancing, much to the joy of the group!'

# Baking fruit scones

Many people will remember baking scones in the past, or enjoying 'cream teas' on summer afternoons. You could use the scones made in this cooking session to have a cream tea at the home or centre. Whilst baking, try to engage people in conversation about their memories. Perhaps you could try asking questions such as:

- Who was the main cook in your family?
- Did you/they only bake on special occasions or all the time?
- Did you have a baking day?
- What were your favourite recipes?
- What were the most economical or simple recipes?
- Did you make anything special for particular events such as children's parties, birthdays or religious festivals?

There are many other good recipes that you could also try, including:

- bread
- shortbread
- mince pies
- cake
- biscuits
- rock cakes

If possible, include a shopping trip to buy ingredients as part of the activity. Take some people from the group with you.

## What is needed

- 450g (1lb) self-raising flour
- 110g (4oz) butter
- 110g (4oz) sultanas
- 50g (2oz) sugar
- 1/2 teaspoon salt
- 1/2 teaspoon bicarbonate of soda
- Milk as required
- Aprons
- Mixing bowls
- Rolling pin
- Baking trays
- Scales
- Oven gloves
- Sieve
- Pastry cutters
- Cooling tray
- Access to oven

## How it is done

• Think carefully about the size and positioning of the group. Some people might enjoy being close enough to watch what is going on without feeling under pressure to participate.

• Ask everyone to wash their hands, including staff members! Also make sure that everyone puts an apron on – this often helps people to realise that a cooking activity is taking place. Then put the ingredients and utensils on the table and take some time to 'explore' these with the group. Before you begin baking, pre-heat the oven to 190°C or gas mark 5.

• Sieve the flour into a large mixing bowl. You could divide the flour up so that several people in the group can help to sieve it. Next, rub the butter into the flour, lifting the mixture to add air to it. Again, people in the group could do this if they wish. Encourage somebody to pour the sugar and the sultanas into the mixture and mix it up. If other people want to help mix, you can pass the bowl around. Finally, add the salt and the bicarbonate of soda, and enough milk to make a soft dough.

• Ask somebody in the group to lightly flour the work surface. Put the dough on the surface and roll it out so that it is about 1 1/2 cm thick. Let everybody have a go at cutting out rounds of dough with the pastry cutters and then place the rounds on the lightly greased baking tray. Bake for 12 to 15 minutes.

• While the scones are baking, everyone in the group can begin to clear away the dirty utensils and wipe down the work surfaces. Try to involve clearing up and doing the dishes in the activity session.

• When the scones are ready, put them on a cooling tray. Why not add clotted cream and jam – another job that people could easily do? When they are cool, enjoy the results of your baking with a cup of tea and congratulate everyone for their hard work. Give yourselves a rating of 1 to 10 on how good people think the finished product is! Perhaps you could also discuss what to bake next time.

**Remember that older people will be used to using pounds and ounces. You might have to convert metric measurements into pounds and ounces if you are using more modern recipe books.**

**Think about ways of dealing with the (unlikely!) event of the end result being a disaster. You could have 'standby' scones waiting in the wings, or perhaps you could just make a joke about what has gone wrong?**

**Remember that some tasks require more manual dexterity, co-ordination and strength than others. Do not give people tasks that are beyond their abilities. However, be careful not to assume reduced ability – some people with dementia will competently roll out pastry**

**if this is a familiar task, even if in some other areas of their life they are very dependent on others.**

**Make sure that you make enough scones for everybody in the home or day centre – also make sure that you tell everybody who made them.**

**If there are people in the group who did not grow up in Britain, try to include recipes from their cultures as well – for example, Naan bread or a Polish cake.**

EXAMPLE

## The benefits of baking

Doris is a new resident in the care home. She is identified by the staff as being unsettled and agitated. Doris used to be a very good housekeeper. One day, a member of staff runs a baking group making scones with four residents. Doris shows some interest in what is going on and is encouraged to join in. The staff member quickly finds her a chair and a bowl with some ingredients. Other members of staff say that she will never sit down long enough to participate. They are right: Doris likes to do her cooking standing up, which is presumably how she has always done things in her own kitchen. The staff try to get Doris to sit down again, but are eventually encouraged to let her do things her own way. Doris prepares 30 scones and sticks to her task for over two hours, cleaning all her utensils and equipment afterwards. She also wipes down the tables and brushes the crumbs up off the floor.

Doris is now part of the home. She helps the domestic staff with cleaning and polishing; she is usually in her apron and often has a duster in her hand. She is always busy and as a result she has now settled in well.

# Making a fruit salad

Sometimes, access to a kitchen or cooker can be problematic, and preparing food that doesn't require cooking can be easier and less time consuming. A fruit salad is also a very healthy choice; many people in care settings do not have easy access to enough fresh fruit.

Making a fruit salad offers good opportunities for discussion about fruits from different parts of the world. This might involve the experiences of people from different cultural backgrounds.

## What is needed

- A good selection of fruit – consider different shapes, colours and textures. Use a mixture of everyday fruit, such as apples and bananas, and exotic fruit, such as mangoes, figs or kiwi fruits. Some fruit – for example, coconuts or pineapples – can provoke humour and conversation about how to open or cut them.
- Enough chopping boards to go round
- Knives – these need to be sharp enough and small enough to be effective. Keep a sharp eye on the number and whereabouts of knives throughout the activity. Always provide appropriate support and supervision.
- A large bowl for the finished fruit salad
- A grater for the zest of some of the fruit
- A lemon squeezer
- Smaller bowls for any discarded skins or pips and any bits that have been in people's fingers and mouths
- Aprons
- A liqueur, such as Amaretto or Cointreau, to add towards the end (optional)

## How it is done

- Make sure everyone washes their hands and puts on an apron before starting.
- Start the session by standing up and peeling an orange in one continuous cutting movement so that the peel hangs down in a spiral. This rarely fails to attract attention and can start conversations about different ways of peeling an orange. Try asking the following questions:
  - How did your mum used to peel oranges for you when you were a child?
  - Did you used to have an orange in a stocking at Christmas?
  - Did you ever stick an orange with cloves?
  - Do you remember the song, 'Oranges and Lemons'?
- Hand round pieces of fruit, bearing in mind that some are easier to peel and cut (like bananas), and some are more difficult (like kiwis or mangoes).
- Staff may need to get people interested by starting to chop or peel a piece of fruit themselves and then asking for the help or advice of a group member.
- Put all the chopped up pieces of fruit in bowl and grate some lemon and orange zest over them. You can also add some orange or apple juice at this stage, or a liqueur if you prefer!
- When the fruit salad is finished, thank everyone for their help and offer them a bowl of their fruit salad. Discuss as a group how well it has worked.

**Some people will only want to watch – this should be respected. Even if people are not physically doing anything, they can still be involved in the social situation and the conversation.**

**Watch the fruit bowl to ensure that contributions to the salad have not been over-fingered or tasted.**

# Cheese tasting

## What is needed

- Various cheeses from different countries
- Cheese biscuits
- Fruit juice (if wished)
- Fruit (if wished)
- Plates/napkins
- A knife

## How it is done

- Take some people with dementia shopping with you to get the cheese.
- Cut the cheese into small pieces (group members can help you do this) and display it on individual plates. Arrange the cheese, biscuits and fruit juice on the table.
- Offer everyone a small piece of cheese to taste, as well as fruit and biscuits if they wish. Try each cheese in turn.
- After tasting each different cheese, discuss it with the people in the group. Did people like the taste of the cheese? What country is each cheese from? Have people tried it before? How much do people think it cost?
- At the end of the tasting, some participants may be able to say which cheese was their favourite. You can help with this, by noting any facial expressions in reaction to particular cheeses!
- Cheese tasting can be a lovely way to finish a meal.

**Be aware of food allergies or preferences – people may be vegan or allergic to nuts and/or dairy produce.**

## Variations

Wine or cocktail tasting can be an enjoyable addition to a cheese-tasting session!

# Making vegetable soup

This is very similar to making a fruit salad. Again, different vegetables can provoke reminiscence and conversation. Try asking people:

- Where did you used to buy your vegetables?
- What were your favourite/least favourite vegetables?
- Did you ever grow your own vegetables?

## What is needed

- A selection of washed vegetables, possibly including leeks, courgettes, onions, aubergines, carrots, mushrooms, celery, peppers, peas, swede and potato – use whichever vegetables you like!
- 2 tablespoons of olive oil or a knob of butter
- Salt and pepper, plus any other spices or seasonings of your choice, such as chilli powder, mixed herbs, bay leaves, dill, grated nutmeg or black pepper
- Vegetable stock cubes
- Corn flour
- Knives and vegetable peelers
- Chopping boards
- A large saucepan
- Grated cheese (optional topping)
- Hot bread rolls

## How it is done

• Pass around some of the vegetables for people in the group to peel and chop. Bear in mind that some vegetables are harder to prepare (for example, onions, potatoes and swedes) and some are much easier (for example, courgettes and mushrooms).

• When all of the vegetables have been chopped up, put them in a big bowl and take them to the cooker. Put the olive oil or butter in a large pan and heat it. Then add the vegetables and sweat them for five minutes. One care worker should stand at the cooker while the vegetables are sweating whilst another person supervises the group with clearing up the dirty utensils and starting on the dishes.

• Once the vegetables have softened up a bit, add enough vegetable stock to cover them all. Stir the soup and add the salt, pepper, bay leaves, herbs etc. Put a lid on the saucepan and let the soup simmer on a low heat for about an hour or until all of the vegetables are soft. If you want to thicken the soup slightly, add the corn flour (mixed with a little water) at the end. You can serve the soup as it is or blend it to make a thick creamy soup.

• If health and safety guidance permits, include the soup in a meal. The people who made it will have a sense of achievement at making some of their own food. Discuss as a group how well you think the session went and discuss how you might do it differently next time.

**Be careful with hot utensils and keep a careful eye on the soup as it cooks. Don't let anyone go to 'check' it without your supervision.**

**Be careful when adding the vegetables to the oil in case it spits.**

## Variations

You can easily adapt this basic recipe by adding chicken pieces and chicken stock to the vegetables, or you can make it thicker by adding lentils and pearl barley. Use your imagination!

# Massage

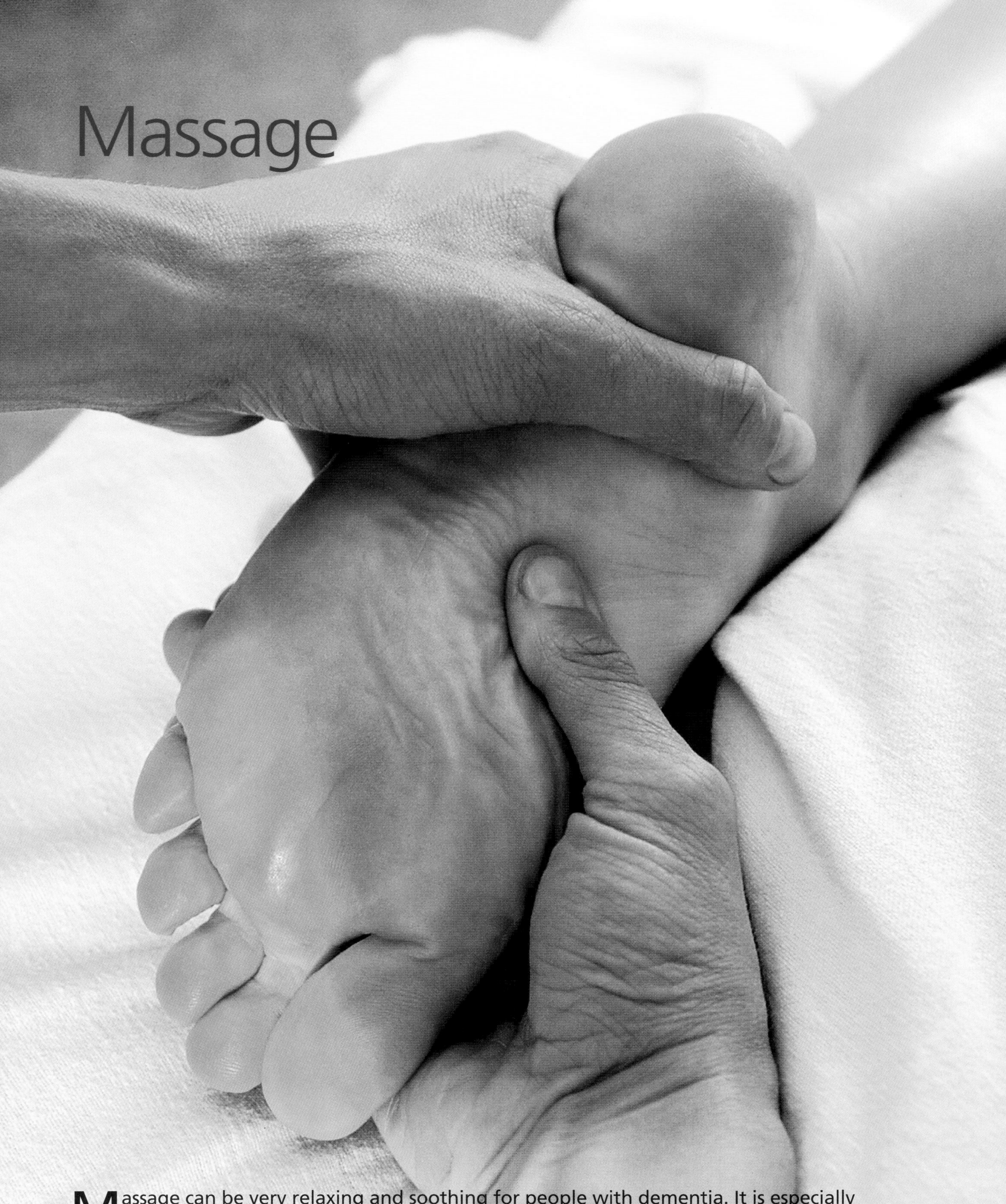

Massage can be very relaxing and soothing for people with dementia. It is especially helpful for people feeling isolated. Although people with dementia may get physical contact through help with bathing and dressing, this is not the same as meaningful and relaxing physical contact. Massage can also have a calming effect on agitated or restless people who may be unable to express their thoughts. It can leave a person feeling more 'in touch' with another human being.

Photo posed by models

## Caution

You should not massage people unless you have appropriate training and/or qualifications. There are many short and inexpensive professional qualifying International Therapy Examination Council (ITEC) courses available in schools and colleges of adult education. However, if you do not have a qualification, rubbing some cream into a person's hands or feet can still be very relaxing and enjoyable for them, and you could also do some of the holds described later in this chapter.



## Physiological benefits of massage

Massage encourages deep relaxation, and regular massage trains the body to get used to feeling relaxed. This has direct effects on health. When we are stressed, our heart rate and breathing increase and our muscles tense. Eventually, this damages the heart and adrenal systems and can lead to chronic headaches, insomnia, anxiety, skin conditions, poor digestion, low immunity, and many other ailments.

Living with dementia can be extremely stressful as it involves losing some control over one's life, as well as losses of routine, friends, hobbies and self-esteem. Massage can help to counteract stress and enable people with dementia to enjoy better health for longer.

Massage is very good for the skin, and helps to maintain elasticity. It also improves blood circulation, which brings nutrients to the skin and helps the systems of the body to work efficiently. Elderly people often feel the cold due to poor circulation.

Massage can be helpful in dispelling tension headaches and can relax tensed muscles. However, it should not be used in place of physiotherapy for joints that are seizing up.

The digestive system can also be boosted through massage. Many elderly people suffer from sluggish digestive systems, resulting in poor appetite and constipation. However, you should not work directly on sensitive stomachs.

Massage creates 'feel good' sensations, which release endorphins (natural pain killers) in the body, thereby improving arthritic conditions. Gentle massage can also help to relax and smooth out cramped fingers. Massage will not prevent arthritis forming, however.

## Safety factors

A basic health check should always be done before a person is massaged, to make sure there are no contra-indications. If the person is unable to give you basic information about their health, liaise with healthcare staff. If you are qualified, GPs will advise on the suitability of massage provided you get the person's consent. Always consider the following:

- Do not massage people with contagious skin conditions or any other contagious or infectious illness. If a person has a skin condition that is not contagious, such as psoriasis or eczema, ensure the massage does not irritate it further. Use a very mild cream and avoid affected areas.
- Do not massage people with early cancers – some people think that this can encourage the spread of cancer cells around the body. Soothing holds can still be helpful (see below).
- Do not massage people with thrombosis (blood clots).
- People with heart conditions should only be massaged very gently.
- Never massage varicose veins.
- Make sure you are aware of whether the person you are massaging suffers from epilepsy or diabetes, although this will not normally affect the treatment.
- Do not massage people who have a heavy cold or fever.

Elderly people often have sensitive skin and may be underweight. Your touch should be light and gentle. Never use deep pressure on an elderly person, as this may cause bruising. Remember that elderly people often have brittle bones. Areas that are sore or injured and sites of recent surgery should not be massaged.

## Preparing for the massage

Find a private, warm and quiet place to work. Residents' rooms are often the best place. It is harder to massage people in busy rooms with the TV on and other distractions. You can massage people in armchairs or in straight-backed chairs. If somebody is in bed, it can be a good time for massage as they will be relaxed. Make sure that you are also comfortable. Be aware of your posture and of whether you are getting tired. Sit or stand behind the person for head, neck or shoulder massages and sit on a low stool or chair if you are massaging hands or feet. You can improvise, provided you are both comfortable. If necessary, lean the person forward a little by propping a cushion behind them. Enhance the environment by playing some soothing music.

Do not use essential oils unless you are qualified, as some are very strong and can cause headaches and skin irritations. Lavender is very mild and slightly sedative but use sparingly – a drop on your sleeve or wrists is sufficient.

There is no need to undress elderly people for massage and they may prefer to remain clothed. However, working on the skin feels much nicer for both parties, so if you are massaging the shoulders, for example, pull down vest straps or undo a few buttons to expose the shoulder. People being massaged lose heat easily, so keep them well covered except for the area you are attending to.

Always ask the person whether they would like to try a massage. If they are doubtful, offer a hand massage (see below). You will probably be able to tell whether the person is enjoying this or not. Some people do not like being touched by somebody of the opposite sex, so be sensitive to boundaries.

## The basic strokes

Always take your time and be gentle. Your touch should be firm but not uncomfortable. This is particularly important with elderly people who may have little body fat to cushion them. Remember that people with dementia may have difficulty expressing themselves if they are uncomfortable.

**Holds**
Holds are very effective, especially for frail people who may hurt or bruise easily. If you cannot massage a person for medical reasons, holds can provide relaxing, comforting contact. They also provide an excellent way to begin and end massage sessions.

*Shoulder hold*
Gently place your hands on the person's shoulders and rest them there for about 20-30 seconds.

*Head hold*
Place one hand on the person's forehead whilst supporting their head with your other hand at the back of their neck. Rest your hands in this position for about 30 seconds.

*Ending holds*
At the end of each series of strokes, rest your hands briefly. At the end of each sequence gently clasp the area – for example the hands or feet – for a few seconds before releasing the contact.

**Rocking**
If the person seems nervous, try rocking them gently.

**Effleurage**
Effleurage is often used to begin and end a massage. Using this stroke is a good way to spread the cream or oil. Use your whole hands, both of them flowing up together and then outwards. You can use effleurage up the top of the arm and then down the side of the arm, up the front of the leg and down the calf, and up either side of the spine and down a little further out from the spine. Do not apply pressure directly on the spine. Start lightly and increase the pressure very gradually. This allows the other person to get used to your touch and prepares them for the deeper strokes.

**Friction**
Rub your hands quickly up and down the skin. This is stimulating and good for creating heat if the person is getting cold.

**Petrissage**
Petrissage means 'pressing'. Gently press your thumbs or fingertips into the area that you are working on. You can also make small circular movements. This is a good stroke for small tense areas, such as the temples, the forehead, the back of the neck and the shoulders.

**Kneading**
This stroke requires some practice. It is a bit like kneading dough, as its name suggests. Using both hands, pick up the tissue and squeeze it, with one hand and then the other. This is a deep stroke, good for fleshy areas such as the tops of the arms and the trapezius, the big muscle at the top of the shoulders. When working with elderly or very thin or frail people, always knead very gently.

**Thumb rolling**
This is similar to petrissage, but as you press with your thumbs, one after the other, push them upwards slightly in small, rhythmical strokes. This stroke is very good for knotty areas such as the shoulders. Again, be careful not to apply too much pressure.

# Preparing yourself

Massaging is very relaxing for the person giving the massage too. Although you should not give a massage if you are feeling particularly frazzled or exhausted, if you are slightly tired or tense you will benefit. The following exercises will help to calm and 'ground' you and enable you to focus on the other person. The first is a breathing exercise, the second is to sensitise your hands.

## What is needed

- A quiet place

## How it is done

- Take two or three deep breaths. This will help to still your mind, emptying it of distractions and worries, and enable you to focus on the other person and the connection between you.

### The complete breath

- Sit or stand comfortably. Breathe out completely, and then slowly breathe in to your abdomen, filling it up with air from the bottom. Imagine you are filling a jug of water from the bottom. As you fill up with air, allow your stomach and then your ribs to expand. Then slowly breathe out, imagining you are emptying a jug of water from the top, emptying the chest first, then the lower ribs, and finally the abdomen, allowing it to flatten as you breathe out completely.
- Pause for a few seconds between each complete breath.
- Your breathing should be deep, but gentle and easy.

### Energising your hands

- Shake your hands – imagine you are shaking off water.
- Wring your hands.
- Wiggle your fingers. Try wiggling one at a time.
- Clench, relax then stretch your hands.
- Tense and then relax your arms.
- Make circles with your hands. This is good for the wrists.
- Make your hands very soft, and gently hold them over your face or stomach.
- Finally, roll your neck gently from side to side and roll your shoulders backwards and forwards.

# A hands sequence

## What is needed

- A small amount of moisturising cream
- A pillow or cushion

## How it is done

- Sit on a low stool or chair at right angles to the person receiving the massage, and rest their arm on a pillow or cushion to relax it.
- Begin by spreading a little cream upwards over the back of their hand and arm using an effleurage stroke. Do this about six times.
- Massage the elbow using the palm of your hand and a little extra cream. Elbows do not get much attention usually!
- Very lightly petrissage the small bones in the wrist.
- Turn the hand over so it is palm upwards, and stretch out the palm using both your thumbs. Support their hand in yours. Lightly press your thumb into the middle of their palm and hold it there for a few seconds.
- Gently massage the spaces between the fingers. Lightly twist and pull each finger in turn, finishing by very lightly pressing the tip of each.
- Squeeze their whole hand in both of yours and make a few long, sweeping strokes down the back of the hand, towards the fingertips.
- Finish with a gentle hold.
- Repeat with the other hand.

# A neck sequence

## What is needed

- A straight-backed chair for the person receiving the massage

How it is done

- Stand behind the person you are massaging.
- With your outstretched hand, hold the back of their head so that your thumb is behind one ear and your index finger behind the other ear. Gently petrissage behind each ear in this way. Support the forehead with your other hand. Work your thumb and index finger along the back of the neck, gently pressing in the middle of the neck (the occipital ridge).
- Knead the back of the neck with both hands.
- Gently stroke the sides of the neck, sweeping your strokes down towards the spine.
- Finish with a head hold.

**Avoid massaging the spine and throat.**

# A shoulders sequence

## What is needed

- A small amount of cream or oil

## How it is done

- If the person is sitting in a chair, prop them forward slightly using a cushion. If they are lying on their back in bed, it will be very difficult to access the shoulders. If appropriate, ask for help in turning the person on to their side.
- Begin by effleuraging up the top of the back and the whole shoulder area, and out across the top of the shoulder. Do this about six times.
- If the other person seems cold, do a friction rub. They should feel a pleasant warmth.
- Sweep your hands outwards from the neck to the shoulder socket, gradually increasing the pressure slightly. Do this two or three times.
- Knead the crook of the neck and along the top of the shoulder, adjusting the pressure to suit the person. This is most effective if it is done very leisurely. You can also knead the tops of the arms but be careful, as it is easy to hurt this area.
- Rub the side of your hand (the index finger side) up and down just below the shoulder blade. This is very good for dissipating tension.
- Massage the whole shoulder blade area with the flat of your hand in circular movements.
- Gently roll your thumbs over the shoulder blades and up along the sides of the spine.
- Squeeze the upper arms gently a few times. Petrissage gently around the shoulder socket area.
- Repeat the sequence with the other shoulder.
- Finish with a gentle hold.

# A feet sequence

## What is needed

- A cushion or towel
- A small amount of cream

## How it is done

- Make sure the person is comfortable. Rest one foot on a cushion or towel in your lap (this works best if the person is sitting in a chair in front of you), making sure their leg is not too high up for their comfort. You can also do a foot massage on a person who is in bed.
- Hold their foot between your hands for a few seconds. With long strokes, cover the foot with cream.
- Supporting the foot with one hand, rub the heel briskly with your knuckle.
- With one hand, lightly knead the ankle.
- Press all over the sole with your thumbs and fingers.
- Work your index finger and thumb down the sides of the foot. Gently press each toe. This can feel very refreshing!
- Stroke your whole hand over the sole of the foot several times.
- Finish with a hold.
- Do the same with the other foot.

**Always find out about the health of the person's feet before massaging them. If the person cannot tell you, ask the nursing staff. Avoid working on corns or bunions. Do not work on varicose veins or heavily swollen ankles.**

**People can be very self-conscious about their feet, but if they can be persuaded to try a foot massage, they often find it very luxurious!**

# Activities in the later stages of dementia

We cannot know for certain what is going on in the mind of a person with advanced dementia. However, a person may still be able to respond to affection, facial expression, touch, and the intonation and rhythm of voices and music.

If somebody is no longer mobile, has limited verbal communication or is very withdrawn, it can be difficult to think of things to engage their interest. However, it is vital that you make an extra effort to reach out to these people, even if you feel that you are getting very little response.

Set aside one-to-one time with a person in the advanced stages of dementia. Use this time to sit with them, stroke their hand and chat about what is happening outside or about something that you know interests them. Make sure you get your positioning right – can they see and hear you? Is physical contact appropriate? Is the person too hot or too cold? Is their clothing and position comfortable for them?

When providing activities for people with advanced dementia, think about stimulating the senses. Here are some ideas:

- Sing a song or play a piece of music.
- Blow bubbles – a pot of bubbles is very cheap and often provokes interest, playfulness or laughter from even very frail people.
- Read aloud from a book, magazine or collection of poems. Choose topics of interest to that person – for example, a gardening magazine, a James Herriot vet story, a Wordsworth poem or a recipe for jam!
- Talk about the person's family members or friends.
- Take the person for a walk in a park or garden. Pick flowers, leaves, fir cones and so on to show the person (see gardening chapter). Remember that if you are pushing a wheelchair, you are not visible to the person. You may need to stop from time to time and move so that the person can see and hear you more clearly.
- Take the person to a children's playground on a sunny day. Playgrounds are often full of colour, laughter and activity.
- If the person spends a lot of time in bed or in a chair in one room, make the area in the person's range of vision interesting. Could a local artist help more able residents or day centre members paint

EXAMPLE

Mary was in the very advanced stages of dementia. She was sleeping in bed for much of the time and had not spoken for several months, apart from calling out the odd word in her sleep. Her granddaughter, Sarah, was sitting at her bedside one afternoon, gently massaging her grandmother's head and shoulders with lavender scented cream. She chatted occasionally about people and places that she knew and at one point she said, 'I really love you, Gran'. Almost immediately, Mary's eyes opened and she looked very intently at Sarah and said, very clearly, 'That's a great comfort, darling'. She then returned to sleep, saying nothing more until she died peacefully two days later.

an interesting mural on the wall? You could enlarge a photograph of someone or something the person loves and put it near them. A mobile might catch the person's eye if they are lying down. Fresh flowers and fruit are also colourful.

- Change the places where a person sits throughout the day. Spend some time with them near the main entrance or reception area of the home or centre. Try seating people on a reclining chair under a tree or close to a bird table in a garden on a warm afternoon. Some people like to sit close to where the handyman, workman or decorator is working so that they can watch quietly.
- Many people like to watch others doing things or working. Try doing jobs such as preparing food, sewing on name tapes, sorting laundry or making a shopping list, as you sit with the person.
- Find treats for a person that might enable them to enjoy tastes or smells. Soft fruits, ice creams, sorbets, soft drinks or chocolate could all provide pleasure.
- Collect interesting objects, fabrics, balls, feathers, beads – things to catch the eye, stroke, fiddle with or laugh at. Explore these with the person. Sometimes, they may not respond at all, but at other times they might show more interest.

## Helping someone with their personal care

- Help to do a person's hair or manicure in a way that involves and nurtures them.
- Sit down with a person to choose which lipstick or tie they prefer.
- Give a person a gentle head massage as you wash their hair.
- Pamper a person's feet with a foot spa using scented oils.
- Use large, warm, soft and richly coloured towels to wrap a person up in when they come out of a bath.
- Think about the personal care tasks a person can still do for themselves – wiping their face with a flannel, arranging beads around their neck or helping polish shoes with a cloth, for example.
- Use soft lighting, relaxing music and aromatherapy oils to create a cosy atmosphere as a person is getting ready for bed. Sit beside their bed and say something about the day's events. If a person is religious, say a prayer out loud with them.
- It can also be very comforting for some people to be gently held, rocked or hugged before bed.

## The magic of babies, children and animals!

Many older people enjoy fussing over and playing with children and babies.

Dogs and cats can inspire affection in animal lovers. They provide opportunities for contact and can become instant 'friends' who don't make demands or judgments or confuse the person with words and questions.

Perhaps you could invite members of a mothers and toddlers' group to your home or day centre on a regular basis. Also think about 'adopting' a volunteer who owns a friendly dog or cat.

## The use of dolls and soft toys

People have different views on the use of children's toys with people with dementia. There is no right or wrong answer to this issue; much depends on how things are done and on personal preferences. Some people find that cuddling a doll or teddy bear satisfies their need for warmth and comfort. However, others may find this demeaning.

Although there is debate about this issue, we must recognise that dolls and soft toys have been used successfully with people with dementia. They can satisfy the human urge to cuddle and cherish another being. Many people with dementia have no inhibition about directing these urges to an inanimate object, which then becomes a figure of attachment. The quality of this attachment varies – some people view the doll as 'real' and develop a profoundly intense relationship with it. Others enjoy a child-like playfulness with the toy and remain clear that it is 'just a doll'.

It is often a good idea to think beyond initial misgivings about offering someone a doll or a soft toy and just try it. You can do this sensitively by leaving some dolls or toys in a corner of the room and seeing who approaches them. If a person is not mobile, you could place the doll or toy in their lap and see how they react. Some people might show that they are insulted by being given a 'child's toy' by pushing it away or becoming angry. The person's choice should be respected and a note made in the care plan.

# Creating a multi-sensory environment

You could design a multi-sensory room especially for individuals with advanced dementia.

## What is needed (an optional selection):

- You can buy specialist 'Snoezelen' equipment to use in sensory rooms. This includes bubble tubes, fibre optics, lava lamps, tumble tubes, sand pictures, oil film projectors and film images. If you have a budget for it, this can be an exciting specialist service to develop. Specialist equipment can be expensive, however, and is not essential.
- Comfortable chairs with interesting coloured and textured fabrics.
- Massage lotion.
- Things to touch – soft toys, fabrics, fake fur, feathers, wool, drift wood, sea shells, boxes, bubble wrap, Russian dolls, rope or elastic, musical instruments, juggling balls, hot soapy water or warm flannels.
- Sensory cushions can be an effective and more age appropriate alternative to soft toys. They can be bought or made with fake furs, velvets or silks.
- Things to smell, such as almond essence, citrus oils, lavender water and curry powder. Use fresh smells too, such as flowers, fresh lavender, grass cuttings or coffee beans. An aromatherapy burner can be a useful addition.
- Things to taste – sweets, fruit, crisps, hot buttered toast or crumpets, honey, chocolate, different flavoured drinks (such as tropical juices, ginger or elderflower cordials, milkshakes or cocktails).
- Things to look at – photographs, different colours, fairy lights, mobiles, flying kites, colourful fabrics (think about different cultural associations such as Indian saris or Scottish tartans), water features, a fish tank – although this needs a great deal of maintenance so avoid it unless you have a real fish enthusiast in your staff team! Soft lighting can create different atmospheres and moods.
- Things to listen to – relaxing music and sounds, (including birds, the sea, whale songs or chants), musical instruments (such as maracas, tambourines, triangles or drums), a bicycle bell, a clock with a loud tick, wind chimes, rain sticks and so on.
- You could compile tapes with sounds that relate to people's individual sources of pleasure – for example, children playing, animal sounds, a train or the voice of a favourite film star. Be aware that these should be used carefully; they could cause confusion if the person starts looking for the children, animals or train that is creating the noise.

## How it is done

- The atmosphere of the session should be gentle and unpressurised – remember, the person participating does not have to engage with anything if they don't want to.
- If you are using specialist equipment, select just one or two pieces to use when the person enters the room for the first time.
- Let individuals explore the room themselves for a while, if they are able to. See where their eyes, ears or hands lead them! Offer the person things to touch, smell or look at and see how they respond. Never push anything – some people may choose to just sit with their eyes closed or fall asleep. If their posture and facial expression indicate that they are relaxed and comfortable, this is fine.
- Set a time limit for the activity – an hour is usually about right, although ten minutes may be enough for some people.
- Allow people time at the end of the session to re-adjust to a 'normal' environment. Find a quieter spot for them to go while they re-adjust. Returning to a busy dining room or large group after such a relaxing experience might be stressful.

**Not everyone will feel comfortable in a sensory environment. It could worsen the symptoms of a person experiencing hallucinations. Moving light products should never be used with epileptic people.**

**Staff using specialist equipment must have proper training. It is important to avoid either using the equipment too much or not enough.**

**Ensure that the environment is safe and non-threatening. Avoid sudden movements or loud noises and keep your voice calm, soft and reassuring.**

**Give the person time to adjust to the mood of the room.**

**Watch carefully for any non-verbal signs that the person is anxious or apprehensive.**

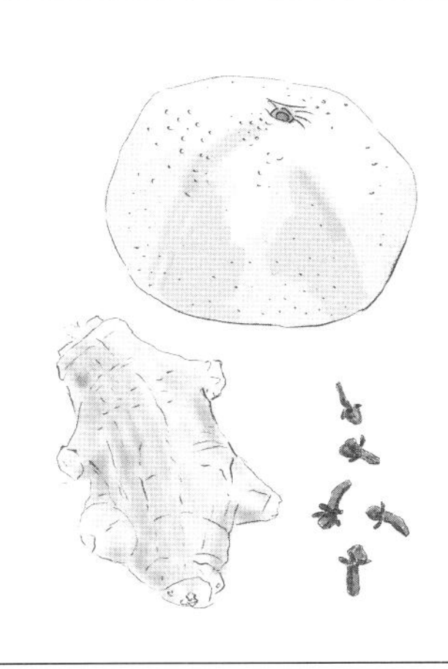

### A Christmas smells box

- Fill small pots with substances that are associated with Christmas and have strong distinctive smells – for example, ginger, marzipan, cloves, mulled wine, oranges, spices, brandy.
- Decorate the boxes with Christmas paper and shiny lids.
- Encourage people to identify the smells and relate them to their own experiences of Christmas. Where possible, allow people to taste the substances as well.

## Variations

The principles of sensory stimulation should not be confined to one room or one activity session. If a person benefits from experiences in a sensory room, adapt other parts of the environment to introduce more sensory experiences. For example, you could create a sensory bathroom or garden using colour, texture, sound and smell.

Create 'sensory boxes' in which to collect different items. These could be a mix of things from the above lists or you could separate them into 'themes' – for example, 'housework', 'seaside', 'DIY' and so on.

Try developing boxes for individual clients, relating them to their background and interests and maybe including personal possessions. These can be added to as you find out more about the person.

# Appendices

Appendix 1

# You as a resource

## Specialist skills needed for activities work with people with dementia

The following skills and qualities are essential for successful activities work with people with dementia. Do you have these skills? Be honest but not too modest!

Rate yourself on a scale of one to four for the following qualities or skills in relation to your work. If possible, give yourself at least one '4' and at least one '1' or '2'.

1 = I do not feel very confident in this area
2 = I think I need to work on improving this skill
3 = I am fairly good at doing this well most of the time
4 = I feel I have a particular strength in this area

| Skills | Your rating |
|---|---|
| Promoting the social and emotional needs of people with dementia in all aspects of daily living | |
| Finding out about individuals' backgrounds and interests and using this knowledge in your work | |
| Explaining clearly what an activity might achieve and giving encouragement and support to those who are initially reluctant to participate | |
| Feeling 'free' enough in yourself to be playful and humorous and to create a sense of fun for the people you work with (where appropriate) | |
| Finding things to talk about and starting conversations | |
| Listening carefully and discovering the feelings behind what someone tries to express – and responding to these | |
| Relating to people with warmth and consideration, even when their words do not make obvious sense to you and the conversation does not follow a logical pattern | |
| Being imaginative about ways to occupy people's time while taking into account individual abilities and interests | |
| Being creative and resourceful and developing a good range of options for activity | |

| Skills | Your rating |
|---|---|
| Providing a structure for activities groups without being over controlling; welcoming and engaging people's interest, involving people with varying levels of ability | |
| Setting aside regular one-to-one time with individuals and making this time special for each person without being pulled to attend to the needs of the wider group | |
| Being flexible – knowing when to drop 'plan A' and think of a spontaneous plan as the opportunity arises | |
| Making the most of the community – finding interesting places for people to visit | |
| Making the most of the community – inviting visitors such as volunteers, musicians and beauticians to the home or day centre | |
| Reviewing the effectiveness and popularity of activities and changing the programme when needed | |
| Working alongside colleagues to develop their skills; motivating and supporting the staff team to take a key role in activity provision | |
| Having a 'healthy humility' and an ability to look at your own skills and approaches in a critical way | |

**The areas I hope to develop in the next year are:**

**I will do this by:** (give examples of action you can take to develop your skills or confidence – for example, visit another home or work with a colleague who you think you might learn from)

# Planning for the future

This exercise may help you to develop some of the ideas that you may have had while reading this book.

## Setting yourself objectives

You might find it helpful to focus on specific areas, for example:

- the range and quality of activity currently available in your home or day centre
- the physical environment in your home or day centre
- work with people in the later stages of dementia or younger people with dementia
- your role-modelling and coaching role with other staff.

For each objective, consider what you need to do and what outcomes you are hoping for.

For example:

| **Objective**<br>What do you want to achieve? | **Action**<br>What do you need to do? | **Desired outcomes**<br>How will you know if you have been successful? |
|---|---|---|
| To raise the profile of the current activity programme in the home | • Make the activities notice board more visually interesting and put it in a more prominent place in the home.<br>• Run an open day for visitors, showing some of the things that residents have been involved in – for example, art work, gardening and dance. | When residents or relatives are asked about what kinds of things are happening in the home, they are more aware of what is on offer. Visitors comment on the activities provision as a positive aspect of the home. |

| **Objective**<br>What do you want to achieve? | **Action**<br>What do you need to do? | **Desired outcomes**<br>How will you know if you have been successful? |
|---|---|---|
| | | |

**Appendix 2**

# Life history notes

## Life history questionnaire

1 Where were you born?
2 What part of the country or the world do you most consider 'home'?
3 What is it about this place that you like and/or dislike the most?
4 What did your parents do for a living?
5 Where did you go to school? Did you like school? What subjects/lessons did you most enjoy or least like?
6 Do you have any brothers or sisters? What are/were their names?
7 Do you have any special friends? What are their names?
8 Who is/was the love of your life? Tell me more about him/her.
9 (If the person is/was married) What was your wedding day like?
10 Do you have any children? Tell me more about them.
11 What did you do for a living? Did you enjoy your work? Looking back now, is there any job you would rather have done?
12 Do you have any religious beliefs?
13 Where did you used to go on holiday or for a day out?
14 Have you ever had/do you have any pets? Tell me more about them.
15 What is your favourite food?
16 What is your favourite drink?
17 What is your favourite type of music or song?
18 Do you have a favourite book?
19 What are your favourite clothes?
20 What is your favourite colour?
21 Tell me about someone you really admire. This might be someone you know personally or a famous person.
22 Do you have any hobbies or interests?
23 Tell me about something in your life you are proud of – however small!
24 What would be your idea of a *real treat*?
25 What sort of things make you laugh?
26 What sort of things make you angry?
27 What sort of things make you embarrassed?
28 What sort of things make you feel upset?
29 What, if anything, do you worry about?

## Likes and dislikes inventory

Filling in this chart might help to give you a better idea of a person's preferences.

| NAME | **Favourite** | **Dislike/least favourite** |
|---|---|---|
| **Colours** | | |
| In general | | |
| For room decoration | | |
| For clothes | | |
| **Music** | | |
| Favourite pieces | | |
| Types of music | | |
| Groups | | |
| Performers | | |
| Instruments | | |
| **Personalities/people** | | |
| Authors | | |
| Politicians | | |
| Actors/actresses | | |
| Singers | | |
| Sports | | |
| Sport figures | | |
| Heroes/heroines | | |
| **Miscellaneous** | | |
| Flowers/plants/trees | | |
| Holiday spots | | |
| Season/s | | |
| Animals | | |
| Books | | |
| Favourite religious texts | | |
| **Food** | | |
| Appetizers | | |
| Meat | | |
| Vegetables | | |
| Desserts | | |
| Snacks | | |
| **Drinks** | | |
| Non-alcoholic | | |
| Alcoholic | | |
| **Activities** | | |
| **Other** | | |
| | | |


This tool is part of the course notes for a 5-day training course, 'Communication and care-giving in dementia:a positive vision'.

## Appendix 3

# Helpful organisations

**National Association for Providers of Activities for Older People (NAPA)**
Unit 211
24/28 Hatton Wall
London EC1N 8JH
020 7831 3320
*Provides support to those with an interest in providing activities for older people. Has a publications list, a regular newsletter and 'Sharing days' which provide contact with others and practical ideas. Is developing a network of regional contacts.*

### ARTS/REMINISCENCE

**Arts Council**
14 Great Peer Street
London SW19 3NQ
020 7333 0100
*Can put you in touch with local artists and give advice on buying arts materials and on general outreach.*

**Age Exchange Reminiscence Centre**
11 Blackheath Village
London SE3 9LA
020 7318 9105
*Runs a community theatre group; hires out reminiscence boxes; runs exhibitions and training; runs specialist groups with people with dementia and their families.*

**British Association of Art Therapists**
Southampton Place Business Centre
16-19 Southampton Place
London WC1A 2AJ
020 7745 7262
*Provides details of training for art therapy students around the country.*

### DRAMA/DANCE AND MOVEMENT/EXERCISE

**British Association of Dramatherapists**
40 Broom House Lane
Hurlingham Path
London SW6 3DP
020 7731 0160
*Provides details of training for dramatherapy students in colleges around the country.*

**Sesame, Central School of Speech and Drama**
Embassy Theatre
Eton Avenue
London NW3 3HY
020 7722 8183
*Provides training in therapeutic movement/drama.*

**Excel 2000**
1A North Street
Sherringham
Norfolk NR26 8LW
01263 825670
*Provides specific exercise for people with disabilities, and training for instructors.*

**EXTEND**
22 Maltings Drive
Wheathampstead
Herts AL4 8QJ
01582 832760
*Runs Extend exercise classes and Extend teacher training courses for movement to music for the over-sixties and disabled people of any age.*

**Disabled Living Foundation**
380-384 Harrow Road
London W9 2HU
020 7289 6111
*Provides information on disability equipment, day-to-day household gadgets, new technologies and training techniques. Also gives expert, unbiased knowledge on the right kind of equipment and where to find it.*

**Jabadao: National Development Agency for Specialist Movement Work,**
Branch house
18 Branch Road
Armley
Leeds LS12 3AQ
0113 231 0650
*Promotes movement as a form of communication. Has a catalogue of props (elastic, parachutes, balls, carnival sticks, tapes etc). Also runs training courses.*

**Foundation for Community Dance**
Cathedral Chambers
2 Peacock Lane
Leicester LE1 5PR
0116 2510516
*Provides details of community dance projects that work with older people throughout the UK.*

**Green Candle Dance Company**
Unit 20.6 Aberdeen Studios
The Aberdeen Centre
22 Highbury Grove
London N5 2EA
020 7357 8776
*Runs workshops and residencies for older people in a range of settings using professional dancers. Provides training in dancing and creative movement with older people.*

**Freedom In Dance**
25 Hawk Green Road, Marple
Stockport SK6 7HU
0161 427 5093
freedom@amans.fsnet.co.uk
*A community dance resource offering training and projects with older people, children, intergenerational groups and disabled people.*

**Medau Society**
8B Robson House
East Street
Epsom KT17 1HH
01372 729056
medau@nascr.net
*Runs a two-year part-time course for teachers of Medau movement and exercise. May be able to put you in touch with a Medau teacher with interest in work with older people in your area.*

## GARDENING

**THRIVE (formerly Horticultural Therapy)**
Geoffrey Udall Building
Trunkwell Park
Beech Hill
Reading RG7 2AT
0118 988 5688
www.thrive.org.uk
*Promotes and supports the use of gardening to improve the quality of life for people with all kinds of need. Provides factsheets, publications, training courses and a quarterly newsletter.*

**The Cottage Garden Society**
Brandon
Ravenshall
Betley
Cheshire CW3 9BH
01270 250776
www.theCGS.org.uk
*Founded to promote interest in cottage gardens, both past and present. Produces 'The cottage gardener', a quarterly magazine, which is also available on audiotape ('The talking cottage gardener'), useful for keen gardeners who have difficulty in reading.*

## MUSIC

**Association of Professional Music Therapists**
26 Hamlyn Road, Glastonbury
Somerset BA6 8HT
01458 834919
*Lists all registered music therapists and can offer details of area co-ordinators.*

**Council for Music in Hospitals**
74 Queen's Road
Hersham
Surrey KT12 5LW
01932 252809
*Arranges and subsidises concerts in hospitals, homes, hospices and day centres.*

**Live Music Now (LMN)**
4 Lower Belgrave Square
London SW1W OLJ
020 7730 2205
*Aims to make live music more accessible to a wider range of people. Due to high demand, performances are subject to LMN having available funding.*

**Music for Life**
Contact: Linda Rose
5 Hurst Close
London NW11 7BE
020 8458 1960
Rhumrose@aol.com
*Offers training and consultancy and interactive music/communication projects for older people with dementia and their care staff.*

## SENSORY

**Multi-sensory Environments Advisory Board**

Group chair: Brigid Barber
Mental Health and Learning Disabilities, Walker Close
Foxhall Road
Ipswich IP3 8LY
01473 275423
*National network of people working in multi-sensory environments. Aims to set standards of practice. Contact Brigid Barber for details of your regional group.*

**SONAS – Activating potential for communication**
38 Belvedere Lace
Dublin
00 353 1 2608138
*A structured programme to activate communication with people with dementia using a multi-sensory approach and extensive use of music and touch. It can be adapted for older people with all levels of dependency.*

## ORGANISATIONS PROMOTING LEARNING OPPORTUNITIES IN LATER LIFE

**National Institute of Adult Continuing Education (NIACE)**
21 De Montfort Street
Leicester LE1 7GE
0116 204 4200
*Promotes adult learning. Projects include 'Learning in Care Settings' and 'Older and Bolder' programmes.*

**Dark Horse Venture**
Kelton
Woodlands Road
Liverpool L17 0AN
0151 729 0092
*An award scheme that recognises new learning achievements by older people.*

**Workers' Educational Association (WEA)**
Temple House
17 Victoria Park Square
London E2 9PB
020 8983 1515
*'Learning for Life' – organises a wide range of courses through a network of staff and part-time course tutors. Community learning programme targets disadvantaged and isolated people, including those in care homes. Regional and local contacts available.*

**University of the Third Age (U3A)**
26 Harrison Street
London WC1H 8JW
020 7837 8838
*Provides a range of study subjects as part of a learning co-operative of older people that enables members to share educational, creative and leisure activities.*

## ANIMALS

**Pets As Therapy (PAT)**
17 Ambrook Road
Reading RG2 8SL
0118 921 2467
*Aims to provide volunteers with dogs or cats to visit care homes, hospitals etc (with their temperament tested and approved). Regional and local contacts available.*

## GENERAL VOLUNTARY ORGANISATIONS WORKING WITH OLDER PEOPLE

**Age Concern England**
Astral House
1268 London Road
London SW16 4ER
020 8675 7200
*Activage Unit supports a range of complementary programmes around the country, including 'Ageing Well', Age Resource and the Intergenerational Network.*

**Help the Aged**
207-221 Pentonville Road
London N1 9UZ
020 7278 1114
*Four strategic priorities: combating poverty (reducing isolation, encouraging inclusion), defeating ageism, (speaking up for our age) challenging poor standards and promoting quality in care.*

**Women's Institute**
N.F.W.I
Denman College
Marcham
Abington OX13 6NW
01865 391991
*Has guest speakers. Organises crafts and writing events.*

**Women's Royal Voluntary Service**
National Headquarters
Milton Hill House
Abingdon 0X13 6AD
01235 442900
*Runs luncheon clubs, and supports older people in a range of settings to maintain their independence and dignity.*

**Townswomen's Guild**
Check local directory.
*Has guest speakers, organises social activities.*

**Oddfellows' Association**
Check local directory.
*Social volunteering.*

**Pensioners' Forums**
Check local directory.
*Retirement issues.*

**Masonic Temples**
Check local directory.
*Social activities and guest speakers.*

**Rotary Club**
Check local directory.
*Fundraising and support to local charities and causes.*

**Variety Club**
Check local directory.
*Fundraising for charities.*

**Contact the Elderly**
15 Henrietta Street
Covent Garden
London WC2E 8QH
020 7240 0630
*A national and regional network of volunteers. Organises monthly trips to a volunteer host for tea. Transport organised through local volunteers.*

**Council for Professions Supplementary to Medicine (CPSM)**
Park House
184 Kennington Park Road
London SE11 4BU
*State registered body for art, music and drama therapists, chiropodists, clinical scientists, dieticians, occupational therapists, speech and language therapists etc.*

**Elderly Accommodation Counsel (EAC)**
3rd Floor,
89 Albert Embankment,
London SE1 7TP
020 7820 1343
*Provides detailed information on all forms of accommodation for older people. Has a database of over 45,000 care homes and sheltered housing places. Also runs national art awards for the over 60s.*

**Counsel and Care**
Twyman House
16 Bonny Street
London NW1 9PG
020 7241 8555
0845 300 7585 (advice line)
*An advice and information service on care issues. Carries out research and campaigning, and organises open training and in-house training for care homes.*

**Relatives and Residents Association**
24 The Ivories
6–18 Northampton Street
London N1 2HY
020 7359 8136
*An organisation for residents in care homes and long-stay hospitals, and their relatives. Provides information and support and produces a range of publications, including an African Caribbean project.*

## Appendix 4

# Useful publications and resources

### GENERAL

**Therapeutic activities and older people in care settings – a guide to good practice**
National Association for Providers of Activities for Older People (NAPA)

**The successful activity co-ordinator**
*Training pack – making the best use of resources to provide activities and leisure opportunities to older people in care homes*
Rosemary Hurtley and Jennifer Wenborn, Age Concern Books
PO Box 232
Newton Abbot
Devon TQ12 4XQ
0870 4422044

**Leisure, later life and homes**
Alison Clarke and Jackie Hollands, Counsel and Care

**Not only bingo – a study of good practice in providing recreation and leisure activities for older people in residential and nursing homes**
Counsel and Care

**Care settings in the heart of the community: building a local resources directory**
Growing with Age project, NAPA

**Involving relatives and friends: a good practice guide for homes for older people**
Julia Burton-Jones, Relatives and Residents Association

**Well-being in dementia: an occupational approach for therapists and carers**
Tessa Perrin and Hazel May, Churchill Livingstone (an imprint of Elsevier Science), Foots Cray, High Street
Sidcup
Kent DA14 5HP
0208 308 5702

**The Pool Activity Level (PAL) instrument: a practical resource for carers of people with dementia**
2nd edition (2002), Jackie Pool, Jessica Kingsley Publishers
116 Pentonville Road
London N1 9JB
020 7833 2307

**The emotional-cognitive care assessment record and planning tool**
*Part of the course notes for a 5-day training course, 'Communication and care-giving in dementia: a positive vision'.*
Gemma MM Jones, 1997 (revised 2002)

**Journal of dementia care**
*Publishes a wide range of articles about creative activity work with people with dementia, including all the topics covered in this book.*
Published by Hawker Publications
2nd Floor
Culvert House
Culvert Road
London SW11 5DH
020 7720 2108

**Activities**
Carole Archibald
**Activities II**
Carole Archibald
*Focuses on activities for men, for those in the later stages of dementia and as a means of challenging difficult behaviour.*
**Activities and people with dementia: involving family carers**
Carole Archibald and Charlie Murphy
All of the above **Activities** series are available from the Dementia Services Development Centre
Iris Murdoch Centre
University of Stirling
Stirling FK9 4LA
01786 467740

### REMINISCENCE

**Reminiscing with people with dementia – a handbook for carers**
Errolyn Bruce, Sarah Hodgson and Pam Schweitzer, Age Exchange Reminiscence Centre

**Reminiscence in dementia care**
edited by Pam Schweitzer, Age Exchange Reminiscence Centre

**The reminiscence handbook – ideas for creative activities with older people**
Caroline Osborn, Age Exchange
Reminiscence Centre

### ART

**Collage and dementia: a practical guide for carers and care workers**
Karen Jarvis, Alzheimer's Society
Gordon House
10 Greencoat Place
London SW1P 1PH
020 7306 0606

**Celebrating the person: a practical approach to art activities**
Claire Craig
**Celebrating the person – activity pack**
Claire Craig
*Contains laminated cards offering step-by-step pictorial guides to specific processes such as marbling or card making.*
Dementia Services Development Centre
University of Stirling (see earlier entry under 'General')

**Getting everybody included**
*A report on 'an action research project involving people with dementia and those who work with them in a creative arts project*
Magic Me
118 Commercial Street
London E1 6NF
020 7375 0961

**The arts and older people – a practical introduction**
Fi Frances, Age Concern Books (see earlier entry under 'General')

**Art for the person's sake**
*A video providing cameos of different artists working with groups or individuals.*
John Killick and Sitar Rose, Dementia Services Development Centre (see earlier entry under 'General')

## DANCE

**Invitation to the dance: dance for people with dementia and their carers**
*A practical illustrated book with suggestions for approaches, props and music.*
Dementia Services Development Centre (see earlier entry under 'General')

## GARDENING

**Gardening is for everyone**
Audrey Cloet and Chris Underhill, THRIVE (formerly Horticultural Therapy)

Growth Point 'In Focus' factsheets, also from THRIVE, include:

**Active in the garden: a guide to involving elderly people in institutional gardens**

**Positive gardening: the benefits for elderly people**

**The caring gardener**

**Winter gardening activities**

**Gardening in homes: a guide for relatives in nursing and residential care homes**
Relatives and Residents Association (see earlier entry under 'General')

**Designing gardens for people with dementia**
Annie Pollock, Dementia Services Development Centre University of Stirling (see earlier entry under 'General')

**A garden for you – a practical guide to tools, equipment and design for older people and people with disabilities**
Fred Walden, Disabled Living Foundation

**Discovering the folklore of plants**
Margaret Baker,
Shire Publications Ltd
Cromwell House
Church Street
Princes Risborough
Bucks HP27 9AA
01844 344301

**The wartime kitchen and garden: the Home Front 1939-1945**
Jennifer Davies, BBC Books

## MUSIC

**Responding to music**
Maria Mullan and John Killick
Dementia Services Development Centre, University of Stirling (see earlier entry under 'General')

**Music therapy in dementia care**
David Aldridge,
Jessica Kingsley Publishers (see earlier entry under 'General')

**Songbooks with large clear print and sing-along tapes**
Winslow Press
Goyt Side Road
Chesterfield
Derbyshire S40 2PH

## EXERCISE AND MOVEMENT

**You can do it – exercises for older people**
Margaret Ruddlesden
Hawker Publications (see earlier entry under 'General')

**Alive and kicking – the carer's guide to exercises for older people**
Julie Sobczak
Age Concern Books (see earlier entry under 'General')

**Promoting mobility with people with dementia**
Rosemary Oddy
Age Concern Books (see earlier entry under 'General')

**Music, movement, mind and body – an exercise programme for dementia patients**
*An illustrated book with accompanying music tape.*
Bridget Watson, Winslow Press (see earlier entry under 'Music')

**More than movement for fit to frail older adults**
*Creative activities for the body, mind and spirit*
Pauline Postiloff Fisher
Health Professions Press
PO Box 10624
Baltimore
Maryland 21285-0624, USA

## DRAMA

**Creative groupwork with elderly people – drama**
Madeline Andersen-Warren, Speechmark Publishing
Telford Road
Bicester OX26 4LQ
Tel: 01869 244644
www.speechmark.net

**Storymaking and creative groupwork with older people**
Paula Crimmens
Jessica Kingsley Publishers (see earlier entry under 'General')

## SPIRITUALITY

**Spiritual care: guidelines for care plans**
Laraine Moffitt and Gaynor Hammond, Christian Council on Ageing Dementia Working Group
33 The Plain
Brailsford, Ashbourne
Derbyshire DE6 3BZ

**Frequently asked questions on spirituality and religion**
*Questions posed by people working in a residential setting for older people, but of interest to all those working with people with dementia*

Christian Council on Ageing
Dementia Working Group
(see earlier entry)

## FOOD

**Eating well for older people with dementia – a good practice guide for residential and nursing homes and others involved in caring for older people with dementia**
*A report of an expert working group*
VOICES
PO BOX 5
Manchester M60 3GE
0870 6080213

**Food, drink and dementia – how to help people with dementia eat and drink well**
Helen Crawley
Dementia Services Development Centre, University of Stirling (see earlier entry under 'General')

**Food glorious food – perspectives on food and dementia**
Edited by Mary Marshall
Hawker Publications (see earlier entry under 'General')

## SENSORY

**Assessment for reaching people with dementia through their senses**
Lesley Ann Wareing
Dementia Services Development Centre, University of Stirling (see earlier entry under 'General')

**Aromatherapy for people with dementia**
Judy Reed
Dementia Services Development Centre, University of Stirling (see earlier entry under 'General')

## OTHER

**English Heritage access guide**
*Information about the access of all English Heritage properties for disabled people.*
PO Box 569
Swindon SN2 2YP

**A review of intergenerational practice in the UK**
Dr Gillian Granville,
The Centre for Intergenerational Practice
Beth Johnson Foundation
Parkfield House
64 Princes Road
Hartshill
Stoke-on-Trent ST4 7JL
01782 844 036

## CATALOGUES WITH ACTIVITIES RESOURCES

**Jabadao**
Branch House
18 Branch Road
Armley
Leeds LS12 3AQ
0113 231 0650
*'Bags of Ideas' catalogue has a wide range of props for movement and dance work such as soft and scented balls, carnival sticks, parachutes, lycra sheets and elastic ropes.*

**Winslow**
Goyt Side Road
Chesterfield
Derbyshire, S40 2PH
0845 9211777
*Health and rehabilitation catalogue with a specific dementia section and a good range of games, group work and quiz books, reminiscence products etc.*

**ROMPA**
Goyt Side Road
Chesterfield
Derbyshire, S40 2PH
0800 056 2323
*Specialises in multi-sensory environments and leisure equipment.*

**Nottingham Rehab Supplies**
Findel House
Excelsior Road
Ashby Park
Ashby de la Zouch
Leicestershire, LE65 1NG
0845 120 4522
www.nrs-uk.co.uk

**Specialist Crafts Ltd**
PO Box 247
Leicester, LE1 9QS
0116 269 7711
www.speccrafts.co.uk
*An art and crafts catalogue.*

**TFH**
5-7 Severnside Business Park
Severn Road
Stourport-on- Severn
Worcestershire
DY13 9HT
01299 827820
www.tfhuk.com
*Specialises in multi-sensory environments including sensory gardens.*

**New World Music**
Harmony House
Hillside Road East
Bungay
Suffolk N935 1RX
01986 781 682
*Has a wide collection of new world music for general relaxation and sensory environments.*

**Music and Memories**
Good Music Record Co
Hays House
Freepost PY2035
PO BOX 99
St Austell
Cornwall, PL25 4BR
08705 110 157
*Has collections of nostalgic music and videos.*